MW00657638

Latinas in NURSING

Stories of determination, inspiration, and trust

Tina Loarte-Rodríguez

Latinas in
NURSING

This book is a compilation of stories from numerous people who have each contributed a chapter and is designed to provide inspiration to our readers.

It is sold with the understanding that the publisher and the individual authors are not engaged in the rendering of psychological, legal, accounting or other professional advice. The content and views in each chapter are the sole expression and opinion of its author and not necessarily the views of Fig Factor Media, LLC.

For more information visit:
Fig Factor Media | www.figfactormedia.com
Latinas in Nursing | www.latinasinnursing.com

Cover Design by DG Marco Álvarez
Layout by LDG Juan Manuel Serna Rosales

Printed in the United States of America

ISBN: 978-19-59989-46-2
Library of Congress Number: 2023914000

FIG FACTOR MEDIA

For all Latinas, who dream of and aspire for better, we believe in you. You are our ancestors' wildest dreams, waiting to be realized.

Table of Contents

Acknowledgments

First and foremost, I want to acknowledge all the female warriors and disruptors who came before me. Your strength, power, and sacrifices paved the way for me and many others. Thank you for resisting the status quo and your persistence for better.

Thank you to Mami, a strong woman who instilled in me the power of education, kindness, and advocacy.

My sincerest and heartfelt gratitude to the inaugural Latinas in Nursing for your bravery in sharing yourselves with us and for your trust in this project and its purpose. I am humbled by your greatness.

Thank you to Jackie Camacho-Ruiz, Fig Factor Media, for your powerful mission and unwavering support. You have expertly guided me on this journey with patience, kindness, compassion, and belief.

A special note of gratitude to our Author Concierge, Izar Olivares, Fig Factor Media, for your steadfast commitment to our work and mission, the contributing authors, and me. This was such a rewarding experience with you.

To my powerful network, support system, and personal board of directors, some of which are featured in this volume, you inspire me, hold me accountable, pick me up, and keep me grounded, genuinely and sincerely. Thank you for having my back.

To my beautiful children, thank you for supporting me and

this project. You are my true north. You can do hard and great things. The sky is the limit. Keep chasing your dreams.

I am immensely grateful to my partner, my soulmate, and my husband, Ian, for his belief in me and this journey, which would not have come to fortition without his support. Gracias Pa.

Foreword

In 2022, I had the distinct honor of meeting Dr. Tina Loarte-Rodríguez, the primary author, at the 47th annual National Association of Hispanic Nurses (NAHN) conference in Miami, Florida. Attending NAHN conferences always brings me great joy, as it is there where I learn about my members' deep passions and their plans for the future. At this conference, she shared her interest in elevating the voices and stories of Latina nurses, and their contributions to the field. As a prominent nursing leader, who has successfully led diverse teams to reach improved health outcomes, she recognized the need to advocate for more diversity and inclusion within the nursing profession and saw this book as the first step to leading this change. She was passionate about bringing together Latina nurses to share their stories as a call to action, for all of us to do more to support and empower underrepresented groups in nursing, and to promote leadership development of Latinas in health care. As the current President of NAHN—an organization that advocates for the professional development of over 300,000 Hispanic nurses across the United States—I know that Dr. Loarte-Rodríguez's initiative to write Latinas in Nursing is a much-needed piece of inspiration for our nursing community.

Throughout my professional leadership journey, I too was in search of a Latina nurse mentor to help navigate my educational and career progression, but oftentimes, this person was not easily found. Early on in my career, I was interested in developing my career to improve health outcomes among the Hispanic community, an aspiration described like many of the stories written throughout this book. But knowing how to have a larger impact within my community was an unknown trajectory for me as a practicing registered nurse. Traditionally, the role of the nurse has been directed toward inpatient care with approximately 63 percent of nurses working in hospitals (Health Resources and Services Administration, 2013). As a result, small numbers of nurses are actively working in advocacy or community settings, with even fewer of those nurses being of Hispanic origin. Villarruel and Peragallo (2004) conducted a descriptive study designed to explore leadership development among Hispanic nurses. Study findings revealed that the participants acknowledged their unique role as advocates for the community and for nursing due to the lack of representation of Hispanics in healthcare. The Hispanic nurses also recognized the powerful influence of mentorship in building relationships and developing leadership skills and the importance of volunteer opportunities in community-based organizations, where leadership skills could be practiced and learned (Villarruel & Peragallo, 2004). This also rang true for me, as I often relied on my network within NAHN, to help me navigate many challenges in my career and served as a place for support y ánimo!

However, limited research addressing interest in community leadership among Hispanic nurses exists or is documented in written form. Which adds to the value of this book for our community. How can we learn from those who came before us, if we don't have a place to learn from them? Especially lessons in leadership, which often go unwritten. Leadership in the community setting is important, as community leadership can lead to nurses participating in policy at the local, state and even national level, with the potential to contribute to large scale systems change. A recent 2023 scoping review highlighted leadership as a concept that was missing from the literature when examining the current state of the science for activism in nursing (Ojemeni, Jun, Dorsen, Gerchow, Arneson, Orofo, Nava & Squires, 2023). Leadership, at any level, is needed by nurses to contribute to improving health outcomes and the quality of care of diverse patient populations. Although nursing research on the impact of Latina leadership on health has not caught up with current practice, the stories in this book shed light to the passion and desire by Latina nurse leaders to advance health equity. This book also begins to document our efforts and builds our visibility in health care as leaders. Latino/a nurse leaders are here—and have been working within our communities as change agents.

In reading this book, I am reminded of the contributions of Latino nurses to our society. I am in awe and appreciative for each person's contribution to the nursing profession and admire their ability to overcome adversity to fulfill their personal mission to improve the health of their families, friends, and community. It is not always easy, in fact, for many. It's extremely difficult. Difficult to push past the unknown, difficult to navigate your career while feeling fear and isolation, difficult to challenge the status quo;

but their presence and actions as demonstrated in their stories, and over time, has brightened my life. I have and will continue to learn a lot from them, and their contributions will continue to have a profound impact on the communities they serve now and into the future. I am deeply humbled to have personally known many of the contributing authors and extend my deepest appreciation to Dr. Loarte-Rodríguez, who played an integral role in bringing this book to life. Let us cherish these stories and carry their lessons with us as these Latina nurses continue to pave the way for future generations of Latino nurse leaders.

With profound admiration and respect,

Adrianna Nava, PhD, MPA, MSN, RN
2021-2024 President, National Association of Hispanic Nurses (NAHN)

References

- Health Resources and Services Administration. (2013). "The US Nursing Workforce: Trends in Supply and Education." Department of Health and Human Services. 1-68. Retrieved from: http://bhpr.hrsa.gov/healthworkforce/reports/nursingworkforce/nursingworkforcefullreport.pdf
- Ojemeni, MT Jun, J., Dorsen, C., Gerchow, L., Arneson, G., Orofo, C., Nava, A. and Squires, AP. (2023). "A Scoping Review of Nursing and Midwifery Activism in the United States." *The Online Journal of Issues in Nursing*, Vol. 23.
- Villarruel, A M and Peragallo, N. (2004). "Leadership Development of Hispanic Nurses." *Nursing Administration Quarterly,* 3, 173-180.

Introduction

I am a Latina in Nursing, a member of the most trusted profession in the United States (US), a highly skilled profession that should be part of decision-making about human beings everywhere.

Unfortunately, my journey has not been easy, like the journeys of too many others. My family and I have been overcoming systemic barriers and racism since before birth. My ancestors' drive and hustle to survive are deeply embedded in my DNA, giving me the superpower to thrive. It helped me to navigate growing up poor in an underserved, high-crime neighborhood. It helps me to navigate various traumas from poverty, violence, mental health, and substance use disorders in my family and community.

My belief in evolving, growing, and improving is my true north. It guides me throughout my eternal educational journey while working full-time, coupled with my activism and advocacy involvement. It helps me to find harmony in my busy and wonderfully fulfilling life as I continue to grow, personally and professionally, as an individual, a partner, and the matriarch of a beautiful family.

2020 was an unprecedented year. We experienced a global pandemic and shutdown, except for healthcare professionals and essential workers, who bore the burden of an inadequate public health infrastructure. As the vice president of nursing at a federally qualified health center, I worked long days with my team and staff, ensuring we had the appropriate information, training, and supplies. I would leave my family at home as I went to our sites and out to our community partners to support our teams, patients, clients, and partners in navigating the rapidly changing recommendations, guidelines, and practices. I would come home exhausted and scared. Am I jeopardizing my family? Did I do enough today?

During this time, we experienced another racial justice movement sparked by the murders of individuals who looked like me and my loved ones. This racial justice movement also spanned the globe. By December 2020, the toll of the pandemic and the continued social injustices, murders, and violence against too many humans forced me to pause, reflect, and search for safety and hope.

During this search, I turned to books, a comforting medium for me. I could not find one book written by or about the thousands of Latinas in Nursing.

Not one.

So, I decided to curate one.

According to the 2020 US Census, Latinos account for 18.7 percent of the US population, with 62.1 million Latinos. That is a 23 percent increase from the 50.5 million Latinos counted in the 2010 US Census. Latinos comprise more than half (51.1 percent) of the US population growth between 2010 and 2020.

There is great power in the Latino population, economically and politically. According to New American Economy, US Latino households earned more than $1.2 trillion, paying $308.5

billion in taxes, including $196.5 billion in federal income taxes and more than $112 billion in state and local taxes.

The 2021 report by Latino Donor Collaborative calculated the total economic output (gross domestic product, or GDP) of Latinos in the United States at $2.7 trillion in 2019, up from $2.6 trillion in 2018, $2.1 trillion in 2015, and $1.7 trillion in 2010. Some perspective: if Latinos living in the United States were an independent country, the US Latino GDP would tie with France for the seventh-largest GDP in the world. The Latino GDP is an engine of economic growth and a broad foundation of support for the larger US economy. The financial contribution of Latinos impacts every corner of the nation.

In 2022, the Pew Research Center estimated 34.5 million Hispanic Americans were eligible to vote, making Latinos the fastest-growing racial and ethnic group in the US electorate since the last midterm elections. The number of Hispanic eligible voters increased by 4.7 million since 2018, representing 62 percent of the total growth in US eligible voters. From 2000 to 2018, Latinos were the biggest drivers of growth in the nation's eligible voter population growth, with increases in all fifty states and Washington, DC. A little over half of all Latinos (53 percent) were eligible to vote in 2020, an increase from 50 percent in 2018.

Let us now look at US registered nurse data. According to the 2022 National Nursing Workforce Survey, of the 4.6 million registered nurses in the US, 6.9 percent identify as Latino. For Latino nurses to mirror the makeup of the US Latino population, there needs to be almost 864,000 more Latino nurse at the time of this book publishing.

To adequately care for this beautiful, diverse, economic, and political powerhouse of a people, there must be a concerted effort from all responsible entities involved in healthcare and healthcare professional training to recognize the potential of Latinos in nursing and make significant, tangible, accountable contributions to the support of our growth. Latinas in Nursing belong everywhere decisions about people are being made.

At a state nursing meeting celebrating Nurses' Month in May 2023, a speaker stated, "Everyone knows a nurse or has at least one nurse in their family." Compared to our population, the number of Latino nurses in the US negates this statement. I did not grow up with a nurse in my family until I became one. I did not know any nurses socially until I became one.

This is the purpose of my book, *Latinas in Nursing.*

The stories curated here are unique to the authors. I am thankful for their trust to share so much of themselves with us. I am humbled by their vulnerability to speak their truths.

Undoubtedly, the stories shared will resonate with many Latinas and non-Latinas alike. These stories are meant to be a source of inspiration and strength. A source for acceptance and validation. A source of energy.

For those who may find issues with our stories, we do not care. This is not about you. This is about us, Latinas in Nursing.

For those of you who have found our stories inspiring, we thank you for your time and support of *Latinas in Nursing.* Our power is limitless. Please continue to support Latinas in Nursing through advocacy, mentorship, sponsorship, and scholarship.

Tina Loarte-Rodríguez, DNP, RN, CIC, CPPS, CPHRM

References:

- Jones, Nicholas. "2020 Census Illuminates Racial and Ethnic Composition of the Country." Census.gov, June 10, 2022. https://www.census.gov/library/stories/2021/08/improved-race-ethnicity-measures-reveal-united-states-population-much-more-multiracial.html.
- Natarajan, Anusha, and Carolyne Im. "Key Facts about Hispanic Eligible Voters in 2022." Pew Research Center, November 18, 2022. https://www.pewresearch.org/short-reads/2022/10/12/key-facts-about-hispanic-eligible-voters-in-2022/.
- Smiley, Richard A., Richard L. Allgeyer, Yetty Shobo, Karen C. Lyons, Rayna Letourneau, Elizabeth Zhong, Nicole Kaminski-Ozturk, and Maryann Alexander. "The 2022 National Nursing Workforce Survey." Journal of Nursing Regulation 14, no. 1 (2023). https://doi.org/10.1016/s2155-8256(23)00047-9.
- "The Economic Contributions of Hispanic Americans." New American Economy Research Fund, September 20, 2021. https://research.newamericaneconomy.org/report/hispanic-spending-power-2021/.
- "2021 LDC U.S. Latino GDP Report." Original Research. Accessed August 21, 2023. https://www.latinodonorcollaborative.org/original-research/2021-ldc-u-s-latino-gdp-report.

LISTEN...

ROXANA C. CHICAS

"Listen to your mentors, patients, and community members and understand the complete message behind their words."

CURRENT POSITION

I am a Latina nurse scientist at a university school of nursing.

WHAT I LOVE ABOUT NURSING

I get to do community-engaged research with a grassroot organization, The Farmworker Association of Florida Inc., and Latino immigrant agricultural workers. It is perhaps one of the most marginalized communities and one that I share some of my background with.

HOW I LEARNED TO BELIEVE IN MYSELF

I was four years old when I arrived in the United States (US) with my mom through the southern border. We emigrated from El Salvador due to the civil war. As El Salvador was ravaged by war, entire villages were destroyed and caused people to be displaced. Leaving El Salvador was not my mom's first choice. It was her last choice after realizing that the opportunity to raise me, feed me, and give me opportunities to thrive were almost non-existent if we stayed. I was undocumented until the age of eighteen, when I obtained Temporary Protected Status (TPS). It is estimated that between 50 percent to 70 percent of the roughly 3 million agricultural workers in the US are undocumented immigrants from Latin America, particularly Mexico and Central America (Farmworker Justice., 2014). They, too, immigrated to the US in hopes of a better future for their children and themselves. Every day they sacrifice their bodies with back-breaking work in an industry that is vital to all of us, yet they experience anti-immigrant sentiment and policies that marginalizes them. Throughout my childhood, I witnessed my family, neighbors, and the Latino community have precarious working conditions in physically unsafe environments that caused them physical injuries. Often, work injuries were not treated due to lack of access to healthcare and immigration status, and employers not interested in helping their injured employees. The wear and tear were noticeable on their bodies and their health. Thus, their health risk arose from the work itself for many immigrants who work outdoors, such as agriculture and construction.

I did not know I could be a nurse until age twenty-seven when I worked at a pediatric office. Growing up, I did not think I could be a professional or get a college education because of my immigration status. So, I searched and found a job at a pediatric office, where I felt needed, valued, and could make a positive difference in the care of patients, particularly Spanish-speaking families. The practice I worked at also had two pediatric nephrologists. I interacted with their patients quite a bit because I scheduled their appointments, obtained insurance prior authorizations, and was regularly the interpreter for Spanish-speaking families. However, it was difficult at times to obtain prior authorizations from insurance companies or answer patient questions because I did not have the foundational knowledge of physiology and much less pathophysiology. But one day, one of the pediatricians told me I could be a nurse! All I needed to do was enroll at a community college that was 5 minutes from the practice. I was in disbelief that a doctor thought I could be a nurse. He saw something in me that I had not recognized in myself yet. He believed in my potential. I thought he must genuinely believe I can do it for him to actually say I can be a nurse. So, it was with this belief in me that I took the step—at age twenty-eight—to enroll at Perimeter College at Georgia State University. Paying for college was a challenge for me. Because I did not have a Permanent Resident Card (Green Card) nor was I a US citizen, I was charged out-of-state tuition. In the state of Georgia, students who do not have a Permanent Resident Card or who are not US citizens are charged out-of-state tuition, which is about three times higher than in-state tuition, despite me living in Georgia since the age of five. Although, I did have TPS, which allowed me to live and work in the US, obtain a driver's license, and Social Security card, Georgia does not differentiate between being fully undocumented students and students who have TPS or Deferred Action for Childhood Arrivals (DACA). To pay for tuition, I continued to work as many hours as possible at the pediatric office, I scheduled my classes in the evenings or weekends, and I enrolled in payment plans. I also figured out that online classes, were more affordable regardless if the school considered the student an out-of-state student. Therefore, I took many of my non-science classes online to reduce the cost of tuition.

Towards the end of my first semester in the nursing program, researchers from Emory University School of Nursing announced the Bridges to the Baccalaureate (BttB) program by the National Institutes of Health. The goal of the BttB program was to identify high-performing minority students to develop research-oriented skills and support them through the associate degree to the baccalaureate in nursing (BSN) and on to a PhD program in nursing to become leaders in the field of biomedical research. This was the first time I had heard that nurses could obtain a PhD or that nurse conducted research! I applied to the program and was accepted. I completed a two-year research fellowship while still in the nursing program at Perimeter College. My mentors during the fellowship encouraged me to apply to the Bachelor of Science in Nursing (BSN) program at Emory University. I followed their guidance, applied, and was accepted into the program. My interest in research developed during the two-year fellowship and during the BSN program. Through these research immersions I learned of the profound health disparities in the agricultural worker population. These experiences led me to pursue a PhD in nursing with a focus in occupational and environmental health of agricultural workers in the US and globally. I finished my BSN in the summer of 2016 and started the PhD program in the fall of 2016 at Nell Hodgson Woodruff School of Nursing at Emory University.

The first three years in the nursing PhD program were challenging. During that time, I felt that I was behind my peers as far as having a defined research question. They also seemed to have a better understanding of research, and their vocabulary was much richer than mine. They all seemed to know exactly what they wanted out of the PhD program. I wondered if I had made the correct decision. Did I belong there?

I overcame these insecurities with the help of my mentor, Linda McCauley. At our first meeting she told me that she did not expect me to have a research question because it would more than likely change. She said we would work together to find an appropriate research question. I learned that I could be honest with her. That it was my obligation to be honest with her about what I did not know so that she could provide appropriate guidance to me. At the end of my first year, she told me I needed to submit a proposal for a pilot grant that was accepting applications. I told her I was happy to write a proposal but that I did not know how to write one. I didn't know what to include, how to format it, or any of the other nuances that proposals require. She said to me, "I will hold your hand very close." I was provided examples of proposals and was given assistance to draft the proposal. Dr. McCauley read it and made suggestions several times until it was ready to be submitted. Not once did she make me feel inadequate or unwelcomed on her team. In fact, she embraced me and provided me with the resources I needed to be successful. Again, I learned from this experience that as a mentee, and I needed to be honest and vulnerable with my mentor with what I did or did not know. I also learned to listen to her guidance and that I could trust her. There were several more instances where I was unsure about what needed to be done. Each time, she met me where I was and provided the guidance that I needed. I tried to always listen to her guidance and not be sensitive to it. These hard and awkward conversations are needed in a mentee-mentor relationship. My hope is to be an amazing mentor like she was to me. She continues to be my mentor and will be forever. Throughout my journey, I have gained other mentors that also have been kind and have dedicated their time to provide me with their insight and guidance. Dr. Vicki Hertzberg and Dr. Jeff Sands have helped shaped me into a promising scientist. They, too, will be lifetime mentors.

There are few Latina nurses with a PhD. And even a smaller amount of occupational and environmental Latina nurse scientist. My research focuses on occupational and environmental health hazards. It seeks to improve the working conditions and health of agricultural workers and other outdoor occupational groups.

These groups are at increased risk of heat-related illness, heat stroke, and kidney dysfunction and are now bearing the brunt of life-threatening and dehumanizing extreme heat health effects—which many more communities will face as climate change worsens.

Many workers in the agricultural and construction industries are Latino immigrants who work in very hot environments. These two occupations have the two highest risk of heat-related death compared to other occupations. The research that I do along with my research team and the Farmworker Association of Florida are shaping the future of climate and occupational health sciences, two of the most pressing fields of scientific inquiry today.

Through our community engaged research, I am exploring and advancing issues with real ramifications for the future of global health, such as the impact of food security, immigration practices, occupational health and safety, global nursing care delivery, and policy (especially climate change and labor policies). My work is contributing to policy and engaging with policymakers through multiple advocacy organizations. I leverage our research findings to help build better polices for workers, migrant populations, and communities most vulnerable to climate change.

Furthermore, my research team reaches Latino workers, engages them in biomedical research, and provides health screenings and education on heat-related illness prevention strategies that are imbedded within the research design. Latinos are under-represented in biomedical research; yet, we have been able to conduct biomedical research with large cohorts of Latinos to better understand heat-related illness prevention and investigate evidence-based interventions for this growing demographic group that is vital to the US economy, culture, and well-being.

My hope is that more Latinas will choose to earn a PhD and do research within their communities. Our communities and the biomedical field need Latina nursing powerhouses who bring energy, timely knowledge, and a phenomenal network of allies, advocates, and community partners to help advance the nursing profession and the health of Latino communities. As Latina nurse scientists, we have diverse perspectives and strength as nursing leaders. We are invaluable to the health of our communities, science, and healthcare delivery.

My advice to overcome obstacles and take the first step into nursing for aspiring Latinas in this field is to believe in yourself and to listen to your mentors, patients, and community members. Also, you should understand the complete message behind their words.

FAVORITE NURSING MEMORY

My favorite nursing memory is winning my first grant from the Sunshine Education and Research Center (ERC) at University of South Florida when I was a PhD student. Winning the grant provided me with the opportunity to advance my doctoral training and conduct a research study to investigate evidence-based interventions to protect agricultural workers from heat-related illness. Another favorite nursing memory of mine is being selected for Fellowship in the American Academy of Nursing (Academy), which is considered to be the nursing profession's highest honor.

REFERENCES

- Farmworker Justice. (2014). Selected Statistics on Farmworkers. Farmworker Justice. https://www.farmworkerjustice.org/wp-content/uploads/2012/05/NAWS-data-factsht-1-13-15FINAL.pdf

BIOGRAPHY

Roxana Chicas, PhD, RN, is an Assistant Professor at the Nell Hodgson Woodruff School of Nursing at Emory University, where she researches occupational and environmental health disparities, investigating the physiological effects of chronic heat exposures among agricultural workers through community-engaged research. Roxana is a first-generation immigrant from El Salvador and once held Temporary Protected Status. In collaboration with the Farmworker Association of Florida, she has led two heat-illness intervention studies using real-time biomonitoring equipment among immigrant agricultural workers in the Southeast US, which has the potential for widespread impact against heat-related illness in vulnerable outdoor workers. As a bilingual bicultural nurse scientist, she is committed to conducting research that informs policy to advance environmental justice, teaching, and mentoring the next generation of Latino students and scientists.

Roxana Chicas, PhD, RN
rchicas@emory.edu
X (formerly Twitter), LinkedIn, Ig, and Facebook: @nursechicas

LEARNING, NURSING, THRIVING

AMBERLYNN PANTOJA

"There were so many times I would doubt myself and my abilities growing up, but my support system had my back...I am genuinely happy."

CURRENT POSITION

I am a postpartum registered nurse.

WHAT I LOVE ABOUT NURSING

I love that there are no limits to what nurses can do and where we can work! We can work bedside, outpatient, in schools, as clinical or classroom professors, as legal consultants, and more. Here's my story, including my journey to becoming a nurse and how my life was changed, so I can help to change the lives of others.

AN EARLY TURNING POINT

I was born and raised in Bridgeport, Connecticut, and I owe so much to my hometown. Being from Bridgeport gave me an awareness of inequality, wealth disparities, and how people of color—especially Black and Latine communities—are mistreated by the society we live in. It made me want to give back to the community that gave so much to me, specifically in terms of healthcare.

I had severe asthma as a child, as did many others from Bridgeport, due to air pollution, factories, and housing full of mold along with other triggers. I spent a lot of time with my primary care provider (PCP) as a child. She was always there for me and my family, helping us understand my asthma and the many medications I needed to stay healthy.

When I was around ten, I idolized my PCP and wanted to do what she did when I grew up. So, I set my sights on being a doctor. When I was a few years older, I learned that those letters "APRN" behind her name on her white coat weren't just for decoration. They had meaning. My PCP wasn't a physician, she was an advanced practice registered nurse!

I felt a lightbulb go off in my head and becoming a nurse practitioner became my life's goal. Of course, my goals have changed since becoming a nurse. Nowadays, I want to continue bedside postpartum nursing until I complete my doctorate degree, then become a professor. I guess it was convenient that the profession I decided to go into involved a lot of schooling, because I always loved school.

While I enjoyed doing well in school on my own, there was a lot of pressure from my dad to also do well. That pressure he put on me was a result of his childhood experiences with education. He was the youngest of three kids born to a Puerto Rican family in Flatbush, a neighborhood in Brooklyn, New York, in the 1970s. From what he's told me of his upbringing, his parents would make him and my tío go to school, but they were never involved in any way. There was no helping with homework or making sure his grades were good. My grandparents never expected much of him, and because those expectations were nonexistent, he wasn't pushed to pursue higher education like my titi was. This isn't to say he couldn't "do it." My dad's one of the smartest people I know. If he had the support, he could've done anything he wanted, and he wanted to do a lot.

Because of that, he pushed me hard to always get straight As, be on the honor roll, be valedictorian—and once I got there, to keep going. It was hard, but after many talks with my dad and sessions with my therapist, I understood why he was that way with me. If my father was the storm, my stepmother and mother were the eye of the hurricane—they were my serenity growing up. If the pressure felt too much, I would go to my stepmother for a hug and to my mother for an ear to listen—and having that support was so essential to my wellbeing. We all need support in our lives, no matter what career or life path we choose.

I always wondered why my stepmother was able to be the calm to my father's storm when it came to raising me, and I think it's because of her own experiences with education growing up.

She was raised by her grandmother, a warm and caring woman who valued education and always supported her in every endeavor. Like my stepmother, my mother was raised by her abuela, but in Puerto Rico until she was eleven. But that's where the differences end because my mom loved school—if even one page of her notebook ripped, she would freak out. I guess she passed on her love for learning and organization to me.

As a result of striving to live up to perfection, I felt isolated like no one understood me or what I was going through. That feeling of isolation continued into my senior year college application season. I felt like I was almost at the finish line (little did I know the finish line doesn't really exist). Since I was the first in my immediate family to go to college, I did this entire process virtually alone—and I knew next to nothing about college except that Yale University was a "great" school; University of Connecticut (UConn) was a "good" school; Georgetown University was from the movie *College Road Trip;* and Housatonic Community College in Bridgeport, Connecticut, was a public community college where I took night classes.

LIFE CHANGING

After getting accepted to a school I researched and fell in love with, I thought I was done with the admissions process; but they only offered me a $24,000 scholarship. My heart broke because I knew the scholarship wasn't enough and I'd have to let that school go. I applied to seven other schools, many of which were local state schools in Connecticut, because I didn't know much else.

My guidance counselor suggested I apply to New York University (NYU) as my "great" school, and I did without knowing much about the school. If I had seen the price tag, I probably wouldn't have even applied at all. Thankfully, I got accepted into NYU with a full ride. My parents and I knew that was it, that was my college. Offers like that don't often happen to low–income Puerto Rican girls with big dreams from cities like Bridgeport (but they should because we deserve them).

College was life changing for me. I had freedom to do what I wanted when I wanted for the first time in my life. I also had fun! College was new and exciting. I was meeting people from all over the globe. I heard new languages, learned about different cultures, and tried foods that were different from the Puerto Rican dishes I grew up eating. I went to Broadway shows, museums, parks, and explored Manhattan with my new friends. For the first time in my life, I didn't have to be perfect—I could make mistakes and discover who I really am.

While I had such an incredible time at the start of college, I also experienced a culture shock. The majority of people I spent my life with were other low-income Black and Latine kids. Suddenly, after eighteen years, I was thrown into a massive city with people of too many cultures and socioeconomic statuses to count. Walking down the block you would come across anything from a free university tote bag to a $5,000 designer handbag used as a backpack. And in the wintertime, $2,000 winter jackets seemed to be the uniform in Manhattan. I felt out of place, like an imposter living amongst wealthy socialites. I eventually found my community at NYU, able to bond through shared experiences, including starting therapy.

Therapy is known as a taboo subject in many people-of-color (POC) households. So, while I would have benefitted starting at a young age, I didn't grow up going to therapy. As soon as I realized my mental health was declining due to the stress of college and life in general, I signed myself up with my university. After going on-and-off for roughly five years, I cannot recommend it enough! Therapy helped me to understand how my childhood affected me into adulthood, and how to put things in perspective and to create positive mindsets. If you're going to nursing school any time soon, therapy could be your saving grace. Nursing school is difficult, and you need to be positive and well to get through it.

Graduating nursing school was one of the proudest moments of my life. All the blood, sweat, and tears finally paid off. I learned everything college could teach me about nursing—and then it came time for me to be an actual registered nurse!

When I started my first job as a postpartum nurse, I quickly learned that while nursing school teaches you a lot, it doesn't teach you how to be a nurse. That knowledge comes from practice. It won't always be smooth—you will make mistakes (I'm speaking from experience here!). But I promise you, once you find your niche and passion in nursing that carried you through one of the most difficult baccalaureate degrees in the world, you will feel fulfilled.

Every single day I fall in love with my job all over again. My interests in maternal child health stemmed from one positive maternity clinical experience. There was always a chance I wouldn't like postpartum nursing once I started it, but there's something so wholesome and special about caring for patients when they've just brought life into the world. I get to teach new parents about caring for newborns and celebrate when they can show me that they understand what I taught—like properly changing a diaper or successfully latching for breastfeeding. It fills me with so much happiness that even on super busy shifts when I don't sit down to chart until 1am (because as a new grad it's 95 percent likely you'll work night shift for a while), I don't mind because I get to do what I love for a living.

FAVORITE NURSING MEMORY

One of my favorite memories of being a nurse happened in February 2023. I was working four nightshifts in a row, and I had the same patient for them all. I spent many hours with her and her baby bent over their bed helping with breastfeeding. I don't have kids nor any experience with breastfeeding—so everything I knew at that point was from working at my job. But that knowledge I had wasn't working for this couplet, so I had to get creative. Me and the mom had a great relationship, and she was open to anything I suggested. On my last shift, I finally got the baby to sustain a latch for a full feeding. Then at the next few feedings, the mom was able to position and latch the baby herself. When I went to make my final rounds, me and the mom both teared up and hugged each other when we said our goodbyes. For her, I was an emotional and physical support during the initial recovery after her cesarean delivery (C-section). For me, she was one of the first patients I really spent hours upon hours taking care of—and her success made me feel like such a good nurse.

Some days I reflect on my life and think about how much it took to get to where I am today. There were so many times I would doubt myself and my abilities growing up, but my support system had my back. In college, I started learning how to stop doubting myself (thank you once again, therapy). After four years, I graduated. Later I passed my National Council Licensure Examination for Registered Nurses (NCLEX-RN®). And finally, I began a job that I am incredibly happy to have. I am thriving and content with my life right now. I have a good relationship with my family and friends, an amazing partner who lifts me up, coworkers who support me and help strengthen my skills as a nurse—and for the first time in a long time I can say that I am genuinely happy.

So that's my story—and it's not anywhere close to being done. A few chapters have gone by, but I'm only twenty-two and have big plans, including a couple of more degrees. So, if you have related to any parts of my story know that you aren't alone, even if it feels like it at times. Support and community can be found in so many places that you might not have even imagined, including school, work, therapy, friends, family, or even online. And once you find your support system, pay it forward and be that for others … you never know who may need a mentor to help guide them through similar experiences.

BIOGRAPHY

Amberlynn Pantoja is a registered nurse (RN) living in New York City and currently works as a postpartum nurse. She graduated from New York University's Rory Meyers College of Nursing in May 2022 with honors from the LEAD Honors Program with a Bachelor of Science in Nursing (BSN). Her passion for nursing, maternal child health, minority health, and LGBTQ+ health began in her hometown of Bridgeport, Connecticut—and she continues to do research to educate herself and others on these topics. She completed a capstone project to educate nursing students on communicating and interacting with, as well as providing care for LGBTQ+ patients. In July 2022, Amberlynn presented on culturally sensitive care for LGBTQ+ Latine individuals for the National Association of Hispanic Nurse's 47th annual conference.

Amberlynn Pantoja, BSN, RN
apantoja5527@gmail.com

I CAN BE A GOOD NURSE

GRACE GRAU

"Anticipate and be ready, for the door may only open once."

CURRENT POSITION

I work for an office of diversity, equity and inclusion (DEI) at a university school of nursing twenty hours per month, and twenty hours per month as a nurse practitioner at a clinic serving uninsured Latinos eight hours per month. The remainder of my time is immersed in service and spending time with family.

WHAT I LOVE ABOUT NURSING

There are so many things I love about nursing. I love that it can be practiced anywhere in the world. I love that there are so many points of entry into nursing and that you can work with people in all settings and all points of life. I love the rich history of nursing and the infinite possibilities and opportunities for nurses to impact humanity. I love nursing because it has provided the perfect venue for me to grow while serving people in their most vulnerable times. Nursing has been as much a blessing for me as I know I have been to many.

Growing up, I wanted to be a teacher. But it was not until high school that my calling would reveal itself. While influenced by many, my passion for nursing was born from a visit to shadow my mother, who worked as a nursing assistant. I was fourteen at the time.

Shortly after the start of her shift, I followed closely behind as she made rounds. She greeted her patient, an emaciated, frail, elderly woman, who was unresponsive. I stood observing intently as she turned the patient, ever so gently, in bed to inspect the linen beneath her. The nonverbal component communicated a healing and caring language, inspiring safety and security. It was by serendipity the moment of enlightenment occurred as I heard my mother murmur under her breath, "We need good nurses!"

The patient had been incontinent of stool and the excrement had begun to dry against her skin. As I think back on that instance, as if frozen in time, I vividly recall thinking, "I could be a good nurse." I had experienced a profound moment, not only in discerning what I wanted to pursue as a future career/profession, but by observing my mother's exemplification of profound respect and compassion for human life. Following, I will attempt to highlight the metamorphosis of my education and career and how, despite the trials and tribulations, I feel truly honored and blessed to have served so many and embraced my cumulative experiences.

PROFESSIONAL ROADMAP: CAREER SUMMARY

My early years were influenced by my father, a very learned man despite only reaching the eighth grade. Papi (daddy) was my greatest believer. While encouraging me to reach for the sky, he challenged me to never forget where I came from once I made it to the top. Through his eyes, I grew up loving school and learning. While I never doubted I would go to college—as one of six children and the daughter of a barber and housewife—I knew that attending college would have to be through my own efforts and resourcefulness.

Despite marrying at the tender age of sixteen, I maintained a decent grade point average, making it possible to qualify for academic scholarships on graduation from high school. I attended the local community college, despite having a baby by the middle of my second semester. Within a year of my son's birth, I went through a divorce resulting from domestic abuse. Despite great adversity, I completed my nursing prerequisites and an emergency medical technician (EMT) certification course. But I was not successful at my first attempt in nursing school. I was one of those students who struggled with reading; by the time I finished reading the second paragraph I'd forgotten what I'd read in the first. Taking exams was another nightmare. Yes, I was that student, you know the one I'm referring to, the one who read into the questions and, worse still, changed answers. In my third semester of nursing—after two unsuccessful attempts in my pediatric theory course—I was told "perhaps nursing is not for you" and advised to try the local vocational school. I felt defeated, confused and frankly, I was afraid. I remember crying all the way home. Too embarrassed to tell anyone, I did what I often did when I felt stressed out; I took a nap. Determined to be a nurse, I applied and was accepted into another nursing program in the area.

I was torn and harried by the thought of raising my son alone, continuing my education and working. Each day presented the challenge of dropping Bobby off at day care. A mere three-year-old, frail and timid, Bobby was already full of strength and courage I could not yet see. Thankfully, my father and mother offered financial and emotional support, and helped care for my son so I could go to school.

Each day presented a challenge. Racing toward the hospital, eyes full of tears; I'd barely make it by 6:45 in the morning. Not having time for guilt, and determined to get an education, I donned my nurse's cap and proceeded to discuss the plan of care for my assigned patients. Desperately wishing the day would end, I would begin shifting gears at two o'clock in the afternoon. By 3:30 p.m. I was out the door, rushing to pick up my sweet little boy. Rush, rush, rush, when would it all end?

It seemed the only time I spent with my son was in the car, driving between school, work, and home. Off we went at 4:30 p.m., time to drop Bobby off at yet another day care and head to work. What trauma patient would rescue bring in today, a victim of an auto accident caused by a drunk driver? A child playing Russian roulette?

My job as an EMT was a blessing in disguise, in many ways a continuation of my clinical practicum, and a great lesson on interdisciplinary collaboration. The respiratory therapist at the hospital where I worked taught me to interpret arterial blood gases, the nurses taught me nursing skills and modeled behaviors of a professional nurse, while the physicians taught me medical terminology and advanced physical assessment techniques. The educational and emotional support my coworkers offered was invaluable, and certainly a great influence on the development of my ethical and professional values. It was during this time, in 1985, I was invited to a NAHN meeting by a work colleague, Luis. It was here, as a student nurse, my journey with NAHN began.

My heart holds a very special place for a counselor at Jackson Memorial Hospital (JMH) School of Nursing in Miami, Florida, for believing in me and for teaching me test-taking skills, time management, and coping strategies. In many ways, I feel she was one of many guardian angels watching out for me. My heart is full of gratitude not only for the exceptional nursing instructors who believed in me, taught me tricks of the trade, and to be accountable, but also for the ones who discouraged me and made me work harder at everything. It was the ones who broke my spirit who led me to lean into my support systems more and taught me what I did not want to emulate.

Finally, the big day arrived, I was a graduate nurse. The

future looked bright, yet deeply seeded in my heart remained the pain that never seemed to leave me, the guilt, a constant reminder of what I put my son through. The large auditorium was full; my body trembled as I walked towards my chair after being pinned. Silence filled the room; suddenly, a little voice said, "Way to go, mom!" The audience's laughter and clapping resonated throughout the room, and it became clear to me, at that moment, the strength and courage my son possessed and the meaning of resilience.

Although I planned to pursue further nursing education, I knew it would be a few years before resuming formal coursework. In the interim, I focused on internalizing my new role as nurse, mastering clinical skills, and building on my foundational knowledge base through self-study and attending local in-services and conferences whenever possible.

Upon graduation, I was hired into a nursing position at the emergency department (ED), where I had been working. Transitioning to my new nursing role was difficult because everyone had been used to my prior role. A life choice made it possible to relocate and begin working as charge nurse in a different ED within six months of graduation. This was where I truly began to develop my role and identity as nurse and leader.

Involvement in hospital committees provided a venue through which I could have a voice, affect practice, and network. Through the years I served on multiple committees, most notably the Tissue Trauma Committee that enabled me to conduct unit research and implement the use of an air mattress following heart catheterization that resulted in the reduction of hospital-acquired pressure ulcers, cost savings, and overall, improved patient outcomes. As an organ procurement advocate in the early 1980s, I was instrumental in acquiring organ donations for recipients, and provided options through which family members of deceased individuals could have closure, or a sense their loved one was valued. As a consultant for Genentech Pharmaceuticals, I educated physicians and nurses on the topic of thrombolytic therapy in acute myocardial infarction. I know the educational presentations positively impacted patient outcomes by helping prepare clinicians, who managed patients with coronary ischemia.

As a child, I had wanted to be a teacher, so the idea of teaching came easily. My efforts began at the bedside with patients and their families. I learned quickly that patients felt valued and empowered when I taught them and encouraged them to be active participants in their care. While working in different units, I created manuals containing articles or other information pertinent to the care of the patient population we were seeing. Initially, the articles were meant to address gaps in my knowledge, but I felt the information was credible and worth sharing, so I created manuals to share with my colleagues.

THE PROFESSIONAL PAUSE

My nursing diploma program did an excellent job of instilling a strong love for knowledge and of encouraging the pursuit of an advanced nursing degree, though it would be over time and incrementally. I was fortunate to obtain a scholarship to attend the registered nurse (RN) to bachelor of science in nursing (BSN) mobility program at the University of Miami, from which I graduated in 1996. My mother died within five months following a two-year battle with metastatic breast cancer. My ground was shaken, and my spirit forever torn. This experience left an indelible mark in my heart and informed my role and commitment to advocate for patient safety.

Two years later, I began taking courses towards an advanced nursing practice degree. I moved to Alabama and, in 2005, completed the acute care nurse practitioner program at the University of Alabama in Huntsville, while working concurrently as a staff nurse in the ED. I secured financial assistance by working as a graduate teacher assistant and teaching pre-licensure clinicals.

A lifelong dream was finally attained at age forty-three when I received my master's degree in nursing from the University of Alabama in Huntsville. In some ways, my success was a way of realizing my mother's unfulfilled dream of becoming a physician assistant, a tradeoff she made to raise us. Envisioning myself as *Dr. Quinn, Medicine Woman,* a popular television show at the time about a female doctor who worked in rural settings, my original choice was the family nurse practitioner track. However, that program was full, and I was subsequently offered a slot in the acute care nurse practitioner track. This degree was transformational and opened doors I never imagined, affording the opportunity to work with patients in both the hospital and outpatient setting while developing expertise in prevention and management of chronic cardiovascular conditions in a rapidly growing cardiology office.

TOWARD SELF-ACTUALIZATION: TEACHING AND PRACTICE

My lifelong dream of teaching became a reality, yet navigating academia proved to be the greatest of all my challenges by far. While fortunate to get a faculty appointment, once again I found myself in a novice role at the age of forty-nine. Academia represented a huge adjustment from my familiar and comfortable clinician role. Not only did I have to learn pedagogy, but I had to learn how to teach distance-accessible courses and strategies to engage students with different learning styles and across various age groups. I felt immense stress and anxiety, overwhelmed at times, and for the first time in my life, I cried going to work. As the first Hispanic faculty in the school, while I didn't realize it at the time, I know I experienced imposter syndrome during this time. While most colleagues were supportive, many were not. Yet I was surrounded by visionary leaders who saw potential where I could not, inspired and supported my growth.

My significant service contributions were thus informed through my roles as advanced practice registered nurse (APRN) and faculty and gained impetus through my work on the Alabama Health Action Coalition during which I became determined to advance "The Future of Nursing Campaign goals." Three and a-half years later, and with a doctorate in nursing practice almost completed, I felt renewed hope. Sometime later, I experienced the benefit of having the title of doctor on my badge, when a physician who previously dismissed my contributions about patient care needs, did a double take after glancing at my badge, listened and acted upon what I had to say.

Through my work on the Joint Committee for Advanced Practice of the Alabama Board of Nursing, I was able to reduce barriers for APRNs resulting in increased approval of practice protocols in underserved communities, expansion of approved procedures (vascular access insertion including intra-aortic balloon pump) and prescriptive authority of restricted drugs (antineoplastics, disease-modifying antirheumatic drugs, and controlled substances).

My priorities in nursing have been to advance leadership and grow the nursing workforce to improve health outcomes and health equity. Leading the implementation of the first professional organization for Hispanic nurses in Alabama (the first of only three in the southeastern United States) meant overcoming insurmountable obstacles. I used an innovative approach leveraging mass gatherings at community events for recruitment and utilized bilingual health screenings to engage nurses in attendance.

My most impactful contributions to improve health disparities and inequities were enacted through service and leadership. As one of very few Hispanic nurses with a doctoral degree in Alabama, and the first to serve on a committee of the Alabama Board of Nursing, my lasting and ongoing contributions reduced barriers, advanced nursing credentialling and education, improved health outcomes and research participation. An active NAHN member for over twenty years and participation in national and international initiatives laid the groundwork to start the Alabama chapter in 2016 and scale up my impact.

By leveraging opportunities, I improved health literacy and equity, research enrollment, nursing recruitment, and professional nursing advancement for Latinos. By using novel community engagement strategies, I enhanced dialogue to generate creative and collaborative solutions to complex challenges in nursing education, health and health care, and contributed to reducing systemic and structural racism. I have disseminated the products of my work and strategies through collaborative partnerships to advance nursing knowledge and inform sound, replicable and sustainable practice changes. For decades, I have been advocating for vulnerable populations.

One thing that has remained clear is the need to pass the torch to the next generation of nurses. My goal presently is to share as much as I have learned, to inspire and to support professional development to carry us forward. My advice to any nurse would be to surround yourself with people willing to mentor and support you, think out of the box, always be ready for the unexpected, dare to take risks, and never let anyone crush your dreams. *¡Sí se puede!* (slogan of NAHN).

FAVORITE NURSING MEMORY

Interestingly, my favorite memories of nursing revolve

around instances where I tended to the human spirit, empowering patients or family members in moments of grief and despair. Without a doubt my favorite nursing memory happened while I was still a student nurse. I had a mother brought to the ED with her stillborn. She was understandably distraught, and I felt there was really nothing I could offer her. But then I remembered something I'd learned in school; during extraordinary circumstances, nurses can perform the holy sacrament of baptism. I asked if she practiced any faith and on learning she was Catholic, I offered to baptize the baby, and she accepted. Sometimes, all we can offer is hope and closure.

BIOGRAPHY

One of six children, Grace Grau, was the first to obtain a college degree in her family. She has since earned degrees as Doctor of Nursing Practice (DNP) and is a board-certified Acute Care Nurse Practitioner (ACNP-BC). She was inducted as Associate to the American College of Cardiology (AACC) and will be inducted as fellow to the American Academy of Nursing (FAAN) on October 7, 2023.

With over forty years' experience in healthcare, Dr. Grau's journey began as an emergency medical technician (EMT) while attending nursing school. She graduated from Jackson Memorial Hospital School of Nursing in 1986, obtained her bachelor of science in nursing (BSN) degree from the University of Miami in 1996, her master's in science in nursing (MSN) degree with a focus in acute care from the University of Alabama at Huntsville in 2005, and completed the DNP from the University of Alabama at Birmingham in 2015.

Dr. Grau's clinical focus was emergency and critical care with a focus in cardiology, which later shifted to acute and chronic disease management and academia. She retired from UAB in December 2021 where she held a dual appointment as nurse practitioner (NP) with the University of Alabama at Birmingham (UAB) medicine in the structural heart and interventional cardiology division and assistant professor UAB School of Nursing (SON), where she taught across all programs, with the last five years in the adult-gerontology acute care nurse practitioner (AGACNP) track. Since leaving UAB SON, Dr. Grau volunteers at the Community of Hope Clinic in Pelham, serves as Adjunct Assistant Professor with UAB SON Office of Diversity, Equity and Inclusion (DEI), and oversees the All of Us grant for the National Association of Hispanic Nurses.

Grace Grau, DNP, ACNP-BC
ggraudnp@gmail.com
Facebook: Grace Grau
LinkedIn: Grace Grau

THANK YOU, DENNY'S

CHELSEA ROJAS

"I can finally breathe again after five years, what felt like an eternity."

CURRENT POSITION

I am a newly graduated registered nurse.

WHAT I LOVE ABOUT NURSING

The connections you get to make with your patients. I love holding their hands, sitting by their beds, and having meaningful conversations with them. Not only am I helping them feel better physically, but I also am responsible for their emotional and mental well-being. No one can fully heal with negativity surrounding them and I am determined to be that little bit of light that they need to push through their road to recovery. I will steer them to focus on the million good things versus the small not-so-good things. And I believe that is something we should all be doing as humans.

A CHANGING PATH LEADS TO HAPPINESS

It is an absolute blessing to be where I am today and to be sharing my journey with you. In elementary school, I claimed that I would someday become a surgeon. Then in sixth grade, the career changed to paramedic. In seventh grade during spirit week, we were allowed to dress up as our dream job. At the time, my dad worked at a hospital in the sterilizing department, and he was able to snatch me some green scrubs along with a bonnet and some shoe covers. That day, in math class, my math teacher showed us an X-ray of his ear after getting a cotton swab stuck in his ear canal. I curiously asked, "Is it still in there?" And one of my classmates said abrasively, "And YOU want to be a nurse?" Of course, the class roared with laughter. I don't remember what I replied. But knowing the twelve-year-old me, I know it was definitely sassy. A year later, I began to volunteer at the local hospital in its sterile processing department (SPD). I didn't need volunteer hours; I was just doing this out of curiosity and boredom. Both my parents worked at the hospital, so they were able to get me this opportunity. I truly appreciate my early exposure to the hospital because I knew immediately that SPD was definitely not for me. It was a large room and I had to organize a ton of sterile tools and supplies. There was a radio though, so the staff let me play whatever station I wanted. As a tween girl, KISS 95.7 was my selection, of course. It made the time go faster and more enjoyable. I was so proud about my volunteering; I would tell people that I was going to "work." My school bus was able to conveniently drop me off at the hospital every Monday. Every Monday I bought a strawberry cheesecake ice cream with the money my mom gave me, and I logged onto Facebook on their public computer in the cafeteria, because using the internet on my Blackberry was absolutely forbidden. The only reason that I could possibly remember these details is because of Facebook memories and my constant status updates at the time.

Fast forward to high school, the greatest four years. I was part of the marching band, which took over my life. I didn't mind because I loved it so much. I played the flute for four years and I earned the position of drill sergeant during my senior year. It was a military-style marching band, and a drill sergeant was the second-highest ranked position. I loved not being the top leader. I had the respect from my fellow bandmates but did not have the responsibilities that the drum major had. At my high school, we had the opportunity to be a part of the Health Academy. These were classes offered to students who had an interest in the healthcare field. It was very science heavy but I loved it. We had guest speakers and visited local hospitals and facilities. I also had the opportunity to enroll in a Certified Nursing Assistant course during my junior year, which then certified me at the end of the year. We had "clinicals" every Monday at local nursing homes. One clinical day, I remember walking into a resident's room and the poor resident was covered with feces and emesis, head to toe. We were partnered up with a classmate and my partner said, "I am not doing that" and walked out. So, I was left alone with a staff member to clean up the resident. I knew what I was getting myself into and I took pride in completing that task. As tough as it was, I still knew that this was the direction that I wanted my life to follow.

In December 2014, I received my first college acceptance letter: Quinnipiac University. I remember my mom and I jumping for joy and Christmas was just around the corner. So, life was good. For some reason, I only applied to three colleges. Thankfully, I got into all of them. The other two were University of Hartford in West Hartford, Connecticut (UHart) and Sacred Heart University in Fairfield, Connecticut. But I had my heart set on Quinnipiac. I remember being told by my mom that Quinnipiac would look so good on a résumé and that influenced my decision. Once Christmas break was over, I went to meet with my guidance counselor. "I don't think Quinnipiac is a great idea, maybe reconsider your options," my guidance counselor told me. I was so confused. I mean, I get it, she's a guidance counselor guiding me. That's her job. She explained that "I will not fit in" due to the majority of the university being white, non-Hispanics. Her office was dark with one lamp on her desk and her wall covered with a bunch of inspirational quotes. Statements like, "You can do it!" "Believe in yourself!" "It's okay to stand out from the crowd" with a picture of a giraffe surrounded by zebras. That's what I was trying to do. But why was she gearing me away from it? I don't remember how the rest of the conversation went, but I do remember the fury that my mom had because she still brings it up to this day.

My mom was the one to introduce me to the career choice of physician assistant (PA). At the time, I didn't know what a PA was or even what I wanted to do. She had known several PAs from her experience in the medical field. The profession seemed great to me. All doctor duties without the several years of school; sign me up! So, I was hooked, a PA I will be. It didn't take much convincing, I was just relieved that I had a plan. Until, of course, I had a crisis about two weeks later. I remember crying on my kitchen floor surrounded by my mom and little sister, "I think I want to be a dental hygienist!!" I screamed. I doubted myself. At that moment, I was not able to see myself as a PA. I thought a dental hygienist would've been cool. A dental hygienist seemed comfortable. I love the outpatient setting and I wouldn't have to make dire decisions in regard to a patient's diagnosis or medications to prescribe. Looking back now, I knew absolutely nothing about dentistry, so I have no idea how that got into my head. I eventually calmed down after my mom joined me on the cold kitchen floor where I was sobbing. My mom convinced me to snap out of it. She told me how random that idea was and that I had absolutely no idea what a dental hygienist did. She was right. I got back on track, I decided to attend Quinnipiac University in the fall of 2015 and become a PA.

I struggled at Quinnipiac. I had made amazing friendships and the campus was small, which I liked. My grades, however, suffered. I was in the top 10 percent in my class in high school, what changed? Well, let's dive in. Those four years were the toughest of my life thus far. All the late nights of studying, thousands of meltdowns, the organic chemistry, the biochemistry, all of it. I studied so little in high school and maintained a GPA of 3.9. Now, I studied all night and yet I could not keep my grades up. The only place I could study at the time was in our dining room at home (I commuted) because my room wasn't big enough for a desk. If I studied in bed, I would fall asleep. I hated studying in the dining room, especially when it was like 1 a.m. and I heard my mom snoring in her bedroom. I was so jealous of her sleep; I just wanted to sleep. I struggled so much that I ended up writing a scholarship appeal letter at the end of each year because I was in jeopardy of it being taken away due to my poor grades. I needed this scholarship to stay. My advisor at Quinnipiac was much more helpful than my high school guidance counselor. No corny posters on the wall or desk lamps to "set the mood." In my junior year of college, she brought up the idea, "What about nursing?" That was the moment when I first started thinking about changing my career path. I wouldn't dare tell anyone, though. I doubted myself and I don't think there was ever a time during these four years when I wasn't doubting myself. "All you need is microbiology; no organic chemistry, no biochemistry." Sounds convincing. I wish that I had taken her advice, but I didn't. Maybe because I wanted to prove to myself and others that I can do it. Months later, I earned my first A on an organic chemistry exam. There was nothing stopping me.

Homelife had its imperfections, too. During my freshman year at Quinnipiac, my parents divorced. I was the mediator of the family; I was the one who reassured everyone they were OK.

Once my dad moved out, I felt like I was the "man of the house," in a sense. I had to make sure my mom and my little sister were OK. No one asked me to fulfill this role though, I just felt like I had to. I often dreamt about living at college, so I wouldn't have to deal with any of the drama. But my family needed me; and I couldn't leave my bed and home-cooked meals either. I was eventually diagnosed with anxiety and depression. Growing up, I was the positive one, the giggly one. In middle school, a classmate gave me the nickname, Giggles. Although she never stuck with it, I sure did, and I loved it. All my edited pictures on Myspace were splattered with Giggles. I even used it for Hotmail. Going from Giggles to getting diagnosed with depression was quite the identity crisis.

In May 2019, I graduated from Quinnipiac University with a Bachelor's Degree in Health Science and a minor in Spanish. I was so happy to be done with Quinnipiac. Now comes "real life" and the constant, dreadful question of "which PA schools did you apply to?" Let me tell you. I applied to eleven PA schools prior to my graduation from Quinnipiac. I was rejected from five of them. The other six never responded. No email. No call. My graduation cake of a stethoscope and white coat that says "Future PA" felt like a stab in the back, but I made sure no one knew about it. I remember being at Denny's with my mom for breakfast one day, months after graduation. I wanted to come clean and tell her that I no longer want to become a PA. I was nervous about what her reaction would be and the disappointment I will see on her face. I didn't want to throw this news right at her at the beginning of the meal, so I waited until we were halfway through our Grand Slams. But my mom knows me too well. She knew something was up. She beats me to it. "How are PA school applications going?" At this point, I'm turning red, and I feel the waterworks turning on. My heart drops to my stomach and my mouth suddenly becomes dry. We had the world's most attentive waitress that day, but that didn't stop me from my own word-vomit. Why does the thing that I was so scared about feel so good? I knew that I had made up my mind months ago but saying it out loud gives it confirmation. It was a different kind of relief that I had never felt before. My mom's face said it all. She was the one who introduced PA to me, who had all these expectations of me. All of it was down the drain. "So, what are you going to do?" she says in a desperate tone. "I think I want to go to nursing school," I said with absolutely no confidence. My mom wasn't convinced, and I don't blame her. I am a twenty-two-year-old woman who had no idea of what her future would look like and that scared both of us. I told her my plan and we both agreed on it before getting up from the booth that my thighs are stuck to. It was physically painful, but nothing phases me at this point. I can finally breathe again after five years, what felt like an eternity. I finally feel excited about my future, it's a feeling that I had never felt before. Nursing school, it is.

Fast forward to May 25, 2023. I graduated with an Associate Degree in Nursing from Capital Community College in Hartford, Connecticut. It was stressful. But I understood the material and I enjoyed school. There were so many moments that confirmed this career for me.

FAVORITE NURSING MEMORY

Favorite nursing memory so far happened in my last semester of nursing school; I was assigned to a patient who was on comfort measures. During the report, I was told that she has not spoken ever since she arrived, which was the day before. She was very lethargic, not easily aroused, and barely had her eyes open. The primary Registered Nurse (RN) had to insert a catheter in this patient, so I made sure that I stood by her side. She squeezed my hand and her eyes opened, but she never let out a screech. Throughout the whole shift, she was the patient that I spent the most time with. While she was sleeping, I would rub her forehead so that she knew I was there for her. At the end of the shift, when it was time to say goodbye, I went to make sure that she was tucked in. Right before I left, her eyes opened wide, and she muttered the words "thank you." It's moments like these that proved that I know that being a nurse is why I was put on Earth. I couldn't wait to do this for the rest of my life. Life happens the way that it's meant to. Going to the "best" school does not determine the success of your future. There will be several obstacles and people telling you differently. But you must remember that no one else is living your life except for you. I had longed for this happiness, and it was finally here. I was ecstatic to officially be Chelsea Rojas, RN.

BIOGRAPHY

Chelsea Rojas was born and raised in New Britain, Connecticut, by her parents who both immigrated from Costa Rica. Chelsea was the only child until 2004, when she finally earned her baby sister. Being raised in a Hispanic household, she was taught English and Spanish starting at a young age. She completed her primary schooling in 2015 when she graduated from New Britain High School in Connecticut. She then decided to continue her education at Quinnipiac University in Hamden, Connecticut. During college, Chelsea began her work in the medical field. She started at Apple Rehab in Cromwell, Connecticut and Midstate Medical Center in Meriden, Connecticut, as a Certified Nursing Assistant. After that, she became a Medical Assistant at AFC Urgent Care in New Britain, Connecticut, where she worked for five years. Upon graduation from Quinnipiac University in 2019, she earned her Bachelor's Degree in Health Science with a minor in Spanish. Once she realized nursing was for her, she attended Capital Community College in Hartford, Connecticut, in the midst of a pandemic. While at Capital, she was the Vice President of the National Student Nurses Association and Minority Nursing Mentorship Club, where she connected with her mentor, Tina Loarte-Rodriguez. In 2023, Chelsea earned her Associate's Degree in Nursing and will begin her nursing career at Bristol Hospital in Bristol, Connecticut. In her free time, she enjoys spending time with loved ones, her high-school sweetheart of eight years and her fifteen-year-old dog, Lola. She loves to travel, try new foods, and binge-watch reality TV whenever she gets the chance.

Chelsea Rojas, BS, ADN, RN
chelseamrojas@gmail.com

MY SELF-CARE EVOLUTION

FALLON A. LOPEZ

"But without cultivating your identity, self-belief and self-care how can you add your unique individuality to the collective?"

CURRENT POSITION

I am a transplant clinic nurse and CEO of R You Well? LLC.

WHAT I LOVE ABOUT NURSING

We are one of the most trusted professions, both fierce and kind in the most unique way, in how we advocate and care for our patients, communities, and families. Because of our unique perspectives, we are trained to incorporate the full picture of what the patient needs so we can deliver the best care.

JOURNEY TOWARD A HEALTHIER LIFE AND CAREER

It was the day before Christmas Eve. I was in my apartment, alone on the phone with him and I remember those words, "This is not going to work." I knew where this conversation was headed and, although painful to hear, it was exactly the reality check I needed to heal and find me again! This is the story of how I became a Latina nurse wellness leader, started a wellness business, and learned to love and put myself first again. Although cringe worthy in some parts, God used it all for good and is continuing to use it for good! And I hope it inspires you to see the many blessings in the hard lessons you may face in your own journey.

To be honest, in my early nursing years, I struggled for everyone else's approval but MY own. My goal was to make my parents proud and prove to everyone that I was capable of making something of myself. My upbringing left me with a dysfunctional sense of self-worth and belonging. So, becoming a nurse wasn't on my radar as an altruistic and empowering career choice. I did it so I could get away and finally make something of myself. But before I tell you how it later became one of the better decisions in my life—one that stretches and strengthens me every day in a way that I become a better person for it—I have to tell you more about my background before I get to the breakthroughs I learned along the way.

A little bit about me. I am a halfsies: half Texan-Mexican

and half Nicaraguan. Two totally different backgrounds with two totally different Spanish languages, one Spanglish and one more native Spanish. When my parents got married, they believed that due to their differences in Spanish, it would be best to raise us speaking English. Growing up, I was teased for not knowing Spanish like I was "supposed to," but I still got by. It wasn't until starting nursing school that I faced the hard realization that speaking Spanish would have been a huge benefit to me and the patients I took care of on a regular basis. It would help me to connect and to better understand the needs of my Latino patients. I started my nursing journey as a licensed vocational nurse (LVN). It was a tough job. But with only one year of training before I was able to get in the field, it was a quick way to a better opportunity and a new world. Some of my responsibilities included being in charge of up to thirty-plus geriatric patients in a skilled nursing facility. The patients I cared for were not critical but needed my daily nursing skills, such as wound care, medication administration, and reorientation to their daily surroundings. It was a great place to start and I am forever grateful for my journey! I enrolled in the LVN to the Bachelor of Science in Nursing (BSN) bridge program about three years later. I will confess my intentions for going back to school didn't change much. I wanted a broader impact, but I also wanted to prove myself. I struggled with low self-belief and self-confidence. I was only as important as my accomplishments. This belief stemmed from the conditional love I was given in the home, being the "good and obedient daughter" would give me acceptance and the belonging I longed for. But it was all based on what I did or didn't do. My parents had strict expectations of me and pushing for my education was a top priority. So, I worked really hard in nursing school but never believed I was worth it. I struggled with what I now know as imposter syndrome.

Coupled with the gap in my Spanish fluency, at times, I would feel very disconnected from my culture. So, I continued to work really hard to prove myself for my perceived shortcomings. The thing is, living near the border in Texas you are bound to meet many Hispanic and Latino patients who need medical assistance and sadly end up in the healthcare system repeatedly. Due to language barriers, many get left behind. These racial disparities became more apparent after graduating with my BSN, RN, and I landed my dream job in a major hospital in a critical care unit. I found the stress from the role adjustment, poor self-esteem, and lack of cultural competence to be overwhelming. I remember how fresh and naive I was! I had no experience in the role of a nurse in this type of setting. My role had completely changed from a LVN and I remember feeling so overwhelmed by the learning curve. But I was determined. Here is where I would encounter many Latinos coming in and out of the hospital getting by with basic medical care. My passion to help was inspired from what I experienced on this side of the spectrum. I had been so disconnected from my roots as a Latina. Looking back, I was trying to find myself and a big part of my culture was missing. Learning some Spanish helped me regain confidence. By then my curiosity was sparked, what else could I learn and add to my tool belt of resources. I started to get curious about what else I could do as a bedside nurse to better help my frequent flier patients who get stuck coming in and out of the medical system.

Although I knew the problem was bigger than me, I wanted to help in a bigger way. At this time in my career, I also was feeling the effects of burnout. I worked in a high stress area, I wasn't coping well, and I was in a toxic romantic relationship. Something had to change and I didn't know what or how but I knew I HAD TO DO SOMETHING. Call it a hunch, a passion, or my lightbulb moment where I took intimidating, huge action toward something I believed in. I made the decision to start a health coaching business in November 2019. As a health coach, I could help my patients in a more personal and preventative way to reduce hospital stays by emphasizing healthy lifestyles. Despite my perceived insecurities, I believed in my ability to solve the problem. Then my breakdown happened the day before Christmas Eve, the "situationship" I was in came crashing to a halt! I knew it was coming, for months he evaded questions about our relationship status. Then I heard him mumble something on the other side of the phone, "This isn't going to work." Although painful in the moment, that extraction from my life was exactly what I needed to let the healing happen.

For so long, I lived for everyone else's approval. I even started my nursing career in hopes of proving to my family and friends that I could make something of myself. As a result, this toxic relationship was also a reflection of that. I got so lost in an uncommitted relationship, all in the hopes of keeping it alive when it was clearly dying and taking me with it. My self-worth and belief tanked while in this relationship, but my passion to help people never wavered.

As a Latina, I see how the need to please and lack of an individual identity as a single woman can be part of our cultural influence. It was ingrained in me from a young age, family first. We have a community bond and it can be a strength. Us Latinos, we are known to stick together. We are passionate and community oriented! Even though I didn't learn Spanish until later in life, I inherited a lot of other cultural beliefs and ideas from my family. We hold tightly to family values. But without cultivating your identity, self-belief and self-care, how can you add your unique individuality to the collective? I began to see the idea of individuality was imperative to being a part of a bigger community. And going into my thirties with a major break up, I was learning a huge lesson in Individuality. The break up was just the tipping point, the mass exodus I needed to snap back and learn more about who I was and what I needed to heal and continue in my passion for helping others. Then BOOM! COVID-19 hit a few months later. It was only God's protection that months before, I moved back into my parent's house after the major break up. I was able to be closer to family during that time while still learning about my individuality. It was a special time for me. Like for many when COVID-19 happened, it was a time to get quiet and still and I began to see the importance of mental health and self-care. I had transitioned in my career during this time and started as a travel nurse, so I would pick up small assignments locally in the areas of need. During COVID-19 times, I was on the frontlines. I also was doing my best to heal from a break up, start my NEW business, and keep afloat as a bedside nurse!

ONLY GOD! During this time, it was so uncomfortable I was going against the grain of traditional Latino family views and values. I was even challenging my faith and relationship with God. But I was determined to find myself again. My faith has been a huge part of that journey turning to the truth of who I am in God and who he created me to be. It took that major break up for me to have space to do that work. In order to thrive in that space, I needed a lot of self-care. And I was living it out and learning more about wellness when starting my coaching business. I was embodying what it meant to really care for yourself during the hard lessons of life. Self-care, wellness, and mental health took on a new meaning. I really had to ask myself: How was I treating myself every day? I struggled with switching priorities. I realized if I want to do big things, I need BIG self-care, too. I needed to be intentional about my self- care. What I have learned is that self-care looks different for everyone. My self-care, as a busy go-getter with huge dreams, it is important that I also check my personal self-talk every day. Getting into therapy has given me tools to face those tough times when I want to show up a certain way and I don't. Therapy has really helped me to be kind to myself in my growing process and to redirect thoughts of imposter syndrome. Having healthy relationships and boundaries has been huge for me, because as Latinos we are close and that's great. But it also can become an unhealthy enmeshment. So, I am really processing what it means to me to show up in my relationships, so I still have enough for me and the work I do every day as a nurse and entrepreneur.

This journey to a more healthy, whole version of myself, while still showing up as the impactful nurse I am so driven to be, is not always easy. But now I have the tools and resources to do the work every day. And it all started with letting go of something, someone, an idea, or a belief that no longer served me so that I could make space for something even better. What I learned through this journey and what I am leaving with you is this: There are blessings in those hard lessons, in the no's, in the rejection, in the losses. But it will require the bold moves from you to make the space to see them!

FAVORITE NURSING MEMORY

A patient who became a friend.

During the height of the unknowns of COVID-19, I met a resilient young person, who taught me a lot about perseverance and kindness. I cared for a patient who had suspicious symptoms that resembled COVID-19 but their test results hadn't come back to rule it out. Alone in a makeshift isolation room in the hospital when COVID-19 was surging, we had strict "no visitors" policies. So, when I first walked into the room, covered from head to toe in personal protective equipment (PPE), I did my best to show love and hope with my eyes, the only thing visible. I wasn't scared, I knew the patient was not a threat to me. I was there to help. The patient needed a new IV on my shift and they kept apologizing to me saying, "I'm a hard stick." This wasn't their first rodeo.

Still, I tried my best and after taking my time, reassuring the young person, I was able to find a hidden vein. "Poke," the catheter went in and I was able to give the medication that was needed to decrease swelling and help them breathe. This patient was tough all alone in that room that first night. Despite all the unknowns they never lost the kindness in their eyes. The patient was later confirmed negative for COVID-19 and discharged from the hospital. The full circle moment happened a few months later. The patient sent me a card directly to the unit to personally thank me for taking care of them; it is an amazing testimony of faith and strength. They also shared that they want to become a nurse because of this experience. We are still connected as friends by our love for God, health and wellness and our fur babies. This all happened during one of the toughest times of my nursing career and still I found myself encouraging another amazing soul to follow their life's purpose. Shine bright friends, you never know who you could inspire!

BIOGRAPHY

Fallon A. Lopez, BSN, RN, CCRN, CHWC, is a Registered Nurse, certified Health and Wellness Coach and Personal Trainer. She is a native of Houston, Texas, and the first Latina nurse in her family. Fallon combines her nursing expertise with her passion for health and wellness to create R You Well? LLC. As a result of her own experience with burnout, Fallon underwent a healing journey of her own. This helped her realize that nurses can make a real difference when they begin from a place of health and healing! And now she helps other nurses do the same! It is her passion to help busy nurses create healthy habits with her holistic healing programs focusing on nutrition, fitness, and mindset. Fallon has obtained certifications as a Personal Trainer, Health and Wellness Coach, Diabetes Prevention Coach and Fitness Nutrition Specialist. She is a lifelong learner and continues to invest in her growth with participation in groups, such as Society of Nurse Scientists, Innovators, Entrepreneurs and Leaders (SONSIEL), American Association of Critical Care Nurses (AACN), Prairie View Nurses Alumni Chapter (PVNAC). Fallon also uses her voice and impact as a speaker and podcaster on topics like mental health, fitness, nutrition and spirituality.

Fallon Lopez, BSN, RN, CCRN, CHWC

Fallon@ryouwell.com

IG: Fallonthewellness_RN

BIOGRAPHY

BUILDING YOUR TRAJECTORY IN NURSING WHILE CONTRIBUTING TO THE PROFESSION

AMELIA PEREZ

"Never close your mind to undiscovered possibilities; only you can determine your path."

CURRENT POSITION

I am a professor and department chair at a university school of nursing.

WHAT I LOVE ABOUT NURSING

Nursing is a profession full of diverse opportunities serving individuals and populations to improve their overall health. Whether it is direct patient care or educating students to become the future generation of nurses, nursing is a very rewarding profession. Seeing a patient's condition improve or seeing a nursing student grow professionally throughout nursing school and then into a competent professional nurse are the most rewarding parts of the profession. There are many ways that nurses can succeed in the nursing profession while never losing sight of the overall goal, which is improving health outcomes across populations, whether that is done directly or indirectly.

BLESSINGS IN DISGUISE

I was born in the Dominican Republic and lived there with my father until I was thirteen years old. My father strived to work hard and advance himself with determination to provide the best for his children and to lead by example. Higher education was never a question from the moment I was born. Both of my parents went to college and high school was never viewed as the end point; it was a stepping stone to get to college. When I moved to the United States, I was surprised to see the big celebrations that were tied to a high school graduation, and some of my friends in the United States did not even see college as an option in their mind. Not because of financial barrier, but because they were not interested. That in itself was shocking to me, as I grew up in a country that if you do not go to college, you most likely will not advance professionally. My parents always said that an education is yours forever, no one can take it away, it helps you to be independent, and helps you in communications and interactions with others in society. That has held to be true in my life to this day.

My siblings and I moved to the United States to live with

my mother when I was thirteen years old. My mother had lived in the United States for several years at that point. We moved to a mid-size town in Illinois in the middle of winter. Talk about culture and environment shock! Coming from a tropical island where it is summer all year round, the winter was tough to endure. The skies were gray, the trees were brown with no leaves, and the grass was yellow. In my head, I could not understand how everything looked so bare and colorless yet people lived there happily. As spring came, I started to see the beauty and colors of the United States and began to get excited. The United States has become my home and I am thankful for the many opportunities the country has to offer. As I have traveled throughout the United States, it has been eye-opening and exciting to see such a wide variety of landscapes all within one country. My heart belongs to two homes, the Dominican Republic and the United States. I visit the Dominican Republic once a year and stay very connected to my roots. Every time I arrive, there is nothing like the smell of that ocean breeze and the warmth that is felt not only from the weather, but also from the people. It is like throwing the fish back in its water.

Moving at the age of thirteen to a whole different country was difficult. For the first year, I remember crying often, thinking of the friends and family that were left behind. There were no internet or cell phones at that time. The only connections were an expensive call from a house phone or a letter that would take ten to fourteen days to arrive. My friends and I wrote letters back and forth. My dad called and traveled to the United States often to see us. As the years went on, I adapted to my new life in the United States and never stopped my educational efforts and goals.

The first barrier I encountered in the United States was related to education. When I was a child, there was no minimum age in the Dominican Republic to start kindergarten. When I moved to the United States, I was a sophomore at the age of thirteen. The high school in the United States did not accept that and said that I would need to be placed in eighth grade as that was the "appropriate" grade for my age. My mother and I did not accept that. It would be like regressing and repeating the last three years of my life. My mother contacted my high school in the Dominican Republic and they were able to fax all of my transcripts and necessary information to the high school in the United States. Even after receiving all the documents, the high school in the United States made me take a series of competency tests, all in English, to ensure that I truly was at the intellectual level of a sophomore. I successfully completed all the tests. The principal was in disbelief and apologized to my mom for all the trouble they gave us to be able to start school. Within the next quarter, I was on the high school honor roll list. The principal again told my mom how proud she was and apologized for the initial barriers. We took English classes in the Dominican Republic throughout my childhood, which helped the transition of moving to the United States be a much smoother one.

As I began exploring colleges, I was unsure of my career path. I always knew that I was either going to be an engineer like my dad or a doctor. One day my mom said to me, "Have you ever thought about being a nurse?" She worked with a lot of nurses as she worked in healthcare her entire life and mentioned all the perks and positive aspects of nursing that she had heard from her colleagues. It was a career that had never crossed my mind. I started looking into it and quickly became interested. I began my first two years in a community college as it was a more cost-effective way to complete my general education courses. After that, I got admitted into the nursing program of a university in Illinois and successfully completed my education. I enjoyed my time in college while getting a wonderful education.

As I graduated from nursing school, I was excited for what the future had in store and was ready and determined to fulfill my goals. I took the National Council Licensure Examination (NCLEX-RN®) nursing board exam within two months of graduating and passed with the minimum number of questions possible. I was excited and proud to receive my results. All the hard work was starting to pay off. In regard to securing a job, that was not going so well. At the time, I was too naïve to even imagine the unconscious bias and discrimination that potentially exist in nursing and healthcare. I had a job as a nursing assistant at a small local hospital and had worked there for a year during school demonstrating an excellent work ethic. About eight of us who worked there throughout the hospital were graduating at the same time. I could not understand why they had all been offered jobs near the time of graduation, but I had not been offered one yet. I was told that it was because they all had more seniority than me. I was the only minority in that group of eight graduates.

After some conversations with the manager, she told me that she could probably give me part-time night shift, but that is all she could offer. I was very polite to her. But in my mind, I found this insulting when I knew the other seven were offered full-time positions throughout the hospital. I did not sell myself short as that was not within my goals. I had student loans and living expenses to pay for. I needed a full-time job. I knew that if I searched hard enough, other opportunities would arise.

I applied at numerous hospitals within a one-and-a-half-hour radius from home. I waited and followed up and no one would call. Meanwhile, all my friends kept getting jobs. I did not understand. Finally, within a month, a hospital that was one hour and fifteen minutes away from my home called. I was very excited, went to the interview, and accepted the position. It was a midsize acute care hospital affiliated with a school of medicine. While the distance was not great, especially working five 8-hour night shifts per week (twelve-hour shifts were not widely implemented yet), it was a great opportunity at a much better hospital than where I had been working. I was thankful for the opportunity and began my career on a urology/nephrology/and renal transplant unit. Everyone was welcoming and I learned so much from my patients and colleagues while also providing optimal nursing care to the patients. I was really happy with what I was doing, but the long drive five days a week was starting to take a toll on me. Within six months of working there, my dream hospital at a large metropolitan area finally called from an application I had submitted around the time of graduation. I interviewed and was offered a full-time night-shift position within thirty minutes from home and with three twelve-hour shifts per week on an acute care medicine unit. All the stars were aligning finally! I felt terrible that after seven months, I was leaving the hospital that had opened the doors to me at the beginning of my career. But I also knew I had to look out for my own well-being and the long drive home five days per week after not sleeping all night was becoming unsafe. I started my new job and was so excited! It was a large metropolitan city hospital affiliated with a school of nursing and a school of medicine. The patient-and-staff population was very diverse and I felt like I was at home. There were patients, nurses, doctors, and other healthcare providers from all races and from various countries. Within four months, I was moved to my long desired twelve-hour day shift position. I cannot even describe how thankful I am to that institution as I practiced there as a nurse for fourteen years and encountered patient and collegial experiences that I know I would not have encountered elsewhere. It helped me become the solid nurse and educator that I am today.

I began to realize that sometimes what we think we want is not what is best for us at the time. While I was frustrated not understanding why I did not get the job at the smaller hospital upon graduation, I later realized that there was something much better in store for me and was so thankful that I did not get that job. The diversity in the smaller hospital was almost nonexistent. I was not comfortable there or ever felt welcomed. The resources and technology needed to provide excellent patient care were also very limited. But at the time, I did not know that, because I had not seen better. The moral of the story is that sometimes what we think was a barrier was truly a blessing in disguise.

DON'T LET OTHERS BE YOUR BARRIER

While working as a nurse, I knew I wanted to advance my education and enrolled to complete my Master of Science in Nursing (MSN) degree. My goal was that I could work in hospital education to promote staff development. As I was finishing my Master's degree, without any solicitation, the university I was enrolled in offered me a part-time clinical teaching position. I then realized that sometimes we are making impressions and do not even realize it. Every moment is an opportunity. Teaching college students seemed so scary to me as I was only twenty-six years old and a career in academia had never even crossed my mind. But I told myself, just try it. What if I like it? I enjoyed teaching so much and still do twenty years later. I had found another passion in nursing. Within a year, I was offered a full-time faculty position and began to teach didactic in addition to clinical. I knew that I wanted to do this for the rest of my life. I kept my practice job while I was teaching, working a couple of shifts per month, as direct care was also a passion for me.

Within a couple of years of teaching, the dean asked me what my five-year plan was and if it included a PhD. I told her I would think about it. I attended a promotion and tenure workshop at the university and quickly learned that in order to advance in teaching ranks of promotion and tenure, a Doctorate degree was necessary. I began exploring various PhD programs in the area and was admitted to my program of choice. At first, it seemed dreadful as research was not something I fully enjoyed. Once I began my courses, I gained more knowledge about research, found a topic I was passionate about focused on Hispanic health, and gradually developed an excitement for nursing research. I realized its importance and the impact it can have on advancing health outcomes and the nursing profession. I continue to enjoy research along with my passion for practice and education.

My main advice for success is to not let others be your barrier. Unfortunately, sometimes as a minority in nursing, you do have to prove yourself when you are a beginner. It should not be that way, but I use that as a challenge to show people that we, as Latina nurses, are smart, capable, and successful. People have told me things throughout life to bring me down, but I used it as a challenge instead. Only you can be your own barrier, do not let others determine your path. I was told I was too young to be where I was in my high school education. I was told I was too young to be in a nursing program. One of my graduate faculty stated that I "actually write very well" as if I was expected to have a language barrier or be a poor writer. I was told I was "intimidating" by someone while everyone else said I was welcoming and a great mentor. I was told, "How are you so positive?" with a tone as if it was a bad thing to be positive. I have been called a perfectionist because I have drive and determination. These are a few negative comments, compared to the multitude of positive comments and interactions I have had throughout life. It is all in how you react to it. Do not let the negative people in your life bring you down, focus on the positive, focus on your success!

FAVORITE NURSING MEMORY

I have had so many favorite nursing experiences that I am not sure that I can pinpoint one as the favorite, but I would like to part with some general words of wisdom or lessons that I have learned throughout my professional life:

- Your voice is important! Use your voice to make change, but use it in a polite and respectful way. I used to be quiet and shy early in my career, but quickly realized that if we do not speak, nothing changes.
- Be assertive, but humble. Do not sell yourself short. Know your worth and be assertive about your worth.
- Drive, self-motivation, and determination lead to success. Celebrate even the smallest successes. Life is full of gradual steps so remember to enjoy those steps while you reach your destination.
- Lastly, find your passion. If you work in an area that you are passionate and care about, work automatically becomes enjoyable.

BIOGRAPHY

Amelia Perez, PhD, RN, has been contributing to the nursing profession for twenty-six years. She earned a Bachelor of Science in Nursing in 1996, a Master of Science in Nursing in 2001, and a PhD in Nursing in 2011. She is currently a Nursing Professor and Department Chair. Dr. Perez has been working in nursing education for twenty years. She also worked at a large metropolitan acute care hospital as a Registered Nurse for fourteen years in the area of acute care medicine. Her areas of research expertise include acculturation, health behaviors, hypertension, and health disparities among underserved and underrepresented populations. She also has conducted nursing education and nursing simulation research. Dr. Perez has published articles in peer-reviewed journals and has conducted professional presentations at multiple local, regional, national, and international conferences. In addition to her practice and nursing education background, Dr. Perez serves the nursing profession by maintaining collaborative partnerships with community settings engaging in outreach efforts to improve the health of populations in underserved communities. Dr. Perez is not only committed to excellence in nursing education, research, service, and practice, but also to mentoring, encouraging, and empowering a diverse nursing student body to be the future nursing workforce.

Amelia Perez, PhD, RN
ameliap5317@gmail.com
LinkedIn: Amelia Perez, PhD, RN

ALL ROADS LEAD TO NURSING

SERRITA ROPER

"Nursing is more than a profession; it is an extension of family."

CURRENT POSITION

I am a psychiatric mental health nurse practitioner.

WHAT I LOVE ABOUT NURSING

I love watching the evolution of patients, especially in psychiatric nursing. I love that as nurses, we are most times seeing patients at their lowest and we are able to contribute to their physical, mental, and emotional healing and wellbeing.

FINDING THE RIGHT ROAD

My maternal grandparents migrated from Dorado, Puerto Rico, when my mother was just a toddler. They were one of the first Puerto Rican families to live in our town in Connecticut. Over the years through triumph, tribulation, and perseverance, they built a wonderful life rich in family, culture, and love. Although my grandmother was not formally trained in the medical field, she could cure anything. Sometimes it was as simple as, "Nena, ven aca. Dejame´ ponerte Vicks," because as Latinas we all know the magical healing power of Vicks. Other times she was over the stove making a tea with ginger, honey, and a host of other ingredients. I don't remember exactly what was in the tea, but it was just as magical as Vicks and I swear it cured everything.

When my grandfather was diagnosed with cancer, I was in kindergarten. We lived in Washington DC, while my grandparents and the rest of our family was in Connecticut. I don't remember much about the move, but we returned to Connecticut so my mother could help the family care for him. His care was a family effort. A hospital bed was moved into the living room, space was made for his supplies and, just like that, it became a hospital suite. My grandmother became his nurse navigator and my aunts were her shift nurses. He was sent home on hospice and given six months to live. He lived for almost two years after that. I was seven years old when he passed away. I turned eight a few days later. Looking back at it, that was my very first experience witnessing the power of holistic, compassionate care. That was in 1989.

While my mother was helping my grandfather fight cancer, she was fighting her own battle with drug addiction. Shortly after my grandfather passed away, I'm not exactly sure all that transpired or what events led up to it, but I distinctly remember my mother and stepfather arguing and her leaving with a friend. It would be months before my brother, sister or myself saw her again. At the time, my father was living out of state and did not have a close relationship with his family after my paternal grandmother passed away. It was decided that it would be best if I went to live with my maternal grandmother. So, I went to live with my grandmother, my aunt and my uncle, who was thirteen years old at the time. I don't know how she did it, but my grandmother never missed a beat. She worked and took care of me and my uncle and she just got things done. I'd like to think that I get some of my strength and work ethic from her.

My mother went to rehab and I moved back in with her when I was thirteen years old. I had been classified as gifted and talented when I was in elementary school. By the time I got to middle school, I found that not only was I gifted academically, but socially as well. I learned pretty early on that I could still get passing grades doing the bare minimum. So that's what I did. And that attitude carried me through middle school and high school. By senior year of high school, I wasn't completely sold on the idea of college. I knew I needed to go but I just wasn't sure what I wanted to go to college for. When I was young, I had aspirations to be a pediatrician. That went by the wayside after my first high school biology class. I figured I would enroll part time at a local university as a commuter student to get my feet wet in academia. I unenrolled a few weeks into the semester. I was not meant to be a commuter student, I hated it. So, I decided to take a gap year. I got an apartment with my childhood best friends and I worked two jobs. Three eighteen-year-old girls living on their own. You couldn't tell us anything. We were adulting and it was great!

In the following year, one of my dear friends who was a class under me graduated high school and headed to Clark Atlanta University (CAU) in Atlanta, Georgia. She invited me to take the trip with her and her family to move her in—and I fell in love. That was August 2000. I started to think maybe this adulting stuff was a little overrated. College might be for me after all. Academically, the programs seemed alright, but socially, Atlanta was a dream. It was decided that I was over adulting and it was time to go back to school. In January 2001, at twenty years old, I started my matriculation at CAU, majoring in social work . . . and I did everything but study. The first semester was a social success and an academic bust.

I spent that summer with my father and stepmother in Delaware. Let's just say they were less than pleased with my grades. Given my poor performance, let's just say there was some hesitancy about me going back. To be fair, CAU came with a hefty price tag. To cut costs, instead of living in a dorm, I opted to stay in a rooming house with two friends I had met the previous semester. I was back at CAU. Except now, I started to rethink if I really wanted to major in social work. To be honest, picking a major was secondary as long as I was able to stay in Atlanta. So, I did what any other sensible person would do. I picked the major whose building was closest to where I lived and that is how I went from majoring in social work to majoring in mass communications with a concentration in public relations.

I did better my second year, but truthfully not well enough to make any concrete argument for my father to foot the bill. So that summer, my father dropped the bomb that he would no longer continue to pay for me to continue at CAU. I was devastated, but I entertained the thought of attending other schools. My father set up a tour and interview at Delaware State University. I was accepted on the spot and offered a full ride, so I took it. It was decided. I was closer to my dad and it was free. It was a no brainer...until orientation weekend. Nothing against Delaware State. The campus was beautiful and everyone was so great...but the reality hit. I was going from Atlanta, Georgia, to Dover, Delaware, and let's just say it was a bit of a culture shock. I immediately went into crisis mode. After lots of tears, persuasive arguments, and more tears, my grandmother agreed to cosign on a student loan so I could go back to CAU and off I went.

I had such a great time during my junior year that I became pregnant with twins. I sat out for one semester and tried to return back when the twins were six months old. I lasted about one month into the semester. To say I was overwhelmed is an understatement. I sat out the rest of the semester and then enrolled in summer classes. The twins' father was incarcerated at the end of the fall semester and I was alone in Atlanta with my children. I had one semester left to graduate. I had the option of moving back home to Connecticut and transfer as many credits as I could or buckle down and push through this last semester. I decided to push through and remain at CAU. In 2006, I was a college graduate and a single mother of twin boys.

After graduation, I moved back home to be closer to family and started working as a call center representative for a major health insurance company. I worked there for close to a year, before I found a job with a third-party processor for the Connecticut Department of Social Services as a team lead.

After three years in the position, I was bored. I wanted a position that was challenging and had more growth opportunities. A good friend who was also a co-worker was getting ready to start an accelerated Registered Nurse (RN) program and encouraged me to look into it. I had so many doubts. I was a single mother.

I couldn't afford to work part time. Sciences and math were not my strengths. Just the thought of bodily fluids made me want to gag. I just wasn't sure if nursing was right for me. I talked to my family about it and it was my mother who reminded me that my childhood dream was to be a pediatrician and my grandmother thought it was a great idea. I knew I couldn't do an accelerated program but I was able to find a part-time program that offered evening classes and weekend clinicals. I started to think that maybe this might be doable. So, I applied.

As part of the admission process, students who were trying to get into the nursing program had to attend an informational session about the program. My grandmother passed away one day before the session. My biggest supporter and cheerleader was gone and I thought maybe this is a sign that I should focus on my family and go back to school another time. Then I remembered how proud she was when I told her I was going back to school to be a nurse, and even though she was no longer with us, I still wanted to make her proud. I went to that informational meeting and was fighting back tears the whole time I was there. I made it through the meeting. In the fall of 2012 I started my journey to become a nurse. In December 2015 after all the studying, tears, more studying, and more tears (yes, I cry a lot), I graduated. Then in February 2016, I passed the NCLEX-RN® and officially became a Registered Nurse.

REALITY OF BEING A NURSE

To say I was excited about my first nursing job is an understatement. It was at a nursing home less than a mile from my house. It was perfect! That excitement quickly dissipated after new hire orientation. How could I give quality patient centered care when I had twelve to fifteen patients, and the majority of them were patients with tracheostomies. Sometimes it took the whole morning just to finish the morning med pass. Then there was the charting, wound care, dressing changes, staff meetings, trainings, and more. I was drowning and miserable and I was only about a month in. I started to question if I had made the right choice by going into nursing. Then a patient was wheeled onto the unit that would change everything.

This patient was from Puerto Rico and, much like my grandfather, he arrived with his entire family who also doubled as his medical team. He was in the end stages of amyotrophic lateral sclerosis (ALS). At first, I was so overwhelmed. His family was very clear on the care they expected and his children commuted over an hour every day to bring their mom back and forth so that she could spend each day with him. I knew she was watching my every move. This was her husband of close to if not more than fifty years, and she was going to be there every day to make sure that he received the care he deserved and her children were there as her back up.

In the beginning, it was hard. His wife wanted him out of bed and in a chair. He had special shampoo for his psoriasis on his scalp that needed to be combed through his hair. He was nonverbal, had a trach and a gastrostomy-jejunostomy tube (G-J tube), known as a feeding tube that has both a stomach portion and a small intestine portion. He was a total care patient. I would get so frustrated when his wife would come to the nurse's station questioning when he would be showered, his hair shampooed, or assessed because he looked uncomfortable. I couldn't tell her we were short staffed, or I just spent an hour doing dressing changes, or it was two o'clock and I still hadn't eaten lunch, or I've had to go to the bathroom for the last hour but because I was so busy, I hadn't had a chance and I was probably on the verge of getting a UTI. Sometimes I wanted to run and hide in the med room. Nobody could ask me questions if they couldn't find me. Every night I went home mentally and physically exhausted and wondered if this was what I really wanted to do. This was real life nursing and I no longer had the comforting support of clinical instructors or fellow student nurses to lean on. I was on my own and I questioned everything.

FAVORITE NURSING MEMORY

I was desperate to make this career change work. I started looking at ways to increase my motivation at work. I came across something in an article and one of the questions the author asked was, "What can you do differently?" I thought about that long and hard. I started to think about how much we focused on holistic person-centered care when I was in school. I slowly came to the realization that I was simply looking at this patient as just that a... patient. Completely negating the fact that before his diagnosis and decline, this man worked, was a husband, father, uncle, grandfather and so much more. If I was his wife or child, I would be camped at his bedside as well. As a matter of fact, I had just done that less than a year prior when my grandmother was dying from pancreatic cancer. We're Latina and family is everything. So, in actuality, this family was doing exactly what mine had always done for each other. They were showing up and advocating.

From that moment forward, I made it a point to spark a little conversation with his family each time I went into the room. Even if it was just for the 3 minutes that I was there to change his tube feeding. Over time, I developed a relationship and rapport with the family. The more they got to know and trust me, the less frequent were the trips to the nursing station. They knew that even if I was running a little behind, everything that needed to get done would get done. They trusted me. Over the course of almost a year, we developed the greatest relationship. They became like my second family.

The night that he passed away, the wife insisted that I be notified. When I got the call, my heart sank and I did the same thing I had done when I received the call that my grandmother had passed. I hopped in my car and went to see the family. When I walked into the room, she gave me the biggest hug and burst into tears. We both stood there hugging and crying together. That was the confirmation that I needed to know that I had indeed chosen the right career. This man and his family had taught me so much about empathy, compassion and what patient-centered care truly means. They will always have a place in my heart as they have helped mold me into the nurse that I am today.

BIOGRAPHY

Serrita Roper, MSN, APRN, RN, PMHNP-BC, is a Psychiatric Mental Health Nurse Practitioner in Connecticut. She earned her Associates Degree in Nursing from Goodwin College in East Hartford, Connecticut. She has worked in home care, pediatric specialty care and acute care. She found her love for psychiatry while working part time as a program nurse in group homes for adolescent boys with problem sexual behavior and adolescent girls with significant trauma histories. In 2022, she graduated with a Master of Nursing from University of Saint Joseph University in West Hartford, Connecticut and is a board certified Psychiatric Mental Health Nurse Practitioner. She is currently employed at a local Federally Qualified Health Clinic (FQHC) providing medication management across the lifespan. Serrita is mother to twin boys, Sean and Shane, whom she credits as her biggest motivators. She believes nursing has made her a better mother, friend, sister, and overall better person. She would not be the person she is today had she not chosen nursing as her career path.

Serrita Roper, MSN, APRN, RN, PMHNP-BC

SRoper@Newperspectivesbhw.com

LinkedIn: Serrita Roper

PERSEVERANCE IS MY MEDICINE

CARMEN ROMAN

"Vine, Vi, Y Venci"

CURRENT POSITION

I am a licensed practical nurse (LPN) didactic instructor and an elementary school nurse.

WHAT I LOVE ABOUT NURSING

I love Nursing because I know I am making a difference in many people's lives. Nursing provides me with the opportunity to empower others, learn new things, and meet people from all backgrounds.

I was born in Mayaguez, Puerto Rico. In search of a better life, my parents, two siblings, grandmother, and eleven aunts and uncles moved to the United States. I was two years of age when my journey to a new country began. My parents worked in the tobacco fields as their first employment. My mother attended adult education and obtained her high school diploma at thirty. My father, on the other hand, chose to work.

We took the city bus to buy groceries or attend medical appointments since we had no car. I lived in apartment buildings where property owners neglected the properties. At times, roaches and mice would get into our food, which Mom threw away. My parents provided as best they could with what was available. We never went to bed hungry, felt cold, or lacked the essentials to live. My parents could not afford private schooling; therefore, I attended public schools growing up. My family attended weekly Mass and enjoyed family gatherings. I lived in the inner city of Hartford, Connecticut for forty-six years and recently moved to Windsor, Connecticut. I am one of three family members who have earned college degrees.

Everyone always asked the $1 million question, "What motivated me to become a nurse?" At age eight, I remember sitting in a grey, cold, and gloomy room in the hospital. I had no televisions, books, or toys to play with. My stomach was rumbling and hurting because I had not eaten anything for hours. Even though I could see a small refrigerator in the hallway, I was not allowed to leave the room or offered anything to eat or drink. As I sat beside my mother while she was experiencing an asthma attack, my hunger increased, and my stomach ached. The medical staff entered the room frequently and whispered among themselves. My mother was connected to many beeping machines, intravenous (IV) poles, and tubing for oxygen and treatments. She was wheezing hard and loud. I was terrified for her and myself. I helped her put ice chips in her mouth to quench her thirst. There were times I believed she could have died. Due to the language barrier, she could not communicate with the doctor or nurses. I tried translating for her, but the staff did not acknowledge me. At the time, no interpreter was available. The scenario was the same every time we went to the hospital. Sitting there—alone, frustrated, and scared—awakened my eagerness to become a nurse.

Another reason I became a nurse was to change the statistics and stereotypes held towards Latinas in our community. These statistics and stereotypes included low high school graduation rates due to pregnancies among single mothers and low enrollment numbers in secondary education. These statistics and stereotypes did not deter me from education and changing my life. I graduated high school as a single parent, purchased my first home at the age of twenty-four, and pursued my education in nursing. I am a lifetime learner who continues to break barriers in the Latina community.

My nursing journey began at the immature age of seventeen. I graduated from high school with a diploma and a baby. I enrolled in a Certified Nurse's Assistant (CNA) program and obtained my CNA certificate at Capital Community College in Hartford, Connecticut. However, I believed I could enhance my education. At the age of twenty, with a toddler and a baby on the way, I attended a Medical Administrative Assistant program at Morse School of Business, Hartford, Connecticut and obtained my certificate. While working for a family practice doctor, Mark Belsky, I followed his advice to enroll in college and start my nursing prerequisites. It took me approximately six years to complete them. During that period, I registered and dropped out of the nursing program twice due to the challenges of being a single parent, balancing family life, school, and work. However, in 2006, I graduated from Goodwin College with an Associate Degree in Nursing. With perseverance, in 2015, I enrolled in an online Bachelor of Science in Nursing (BSN) to Master of Science in Nursing (MSN) Track program at Walden University. My eagerness and dedication to learn and educate myself were a priority. I graduated from Walden in 2017 with a BSN and an MSN in 2019.

There were obstacles during my nursing career, which interfered with reaching my goals. They included being a single parent, balancing family life and school, and challenging work. I spent hours studying while my children slept, worked nights, and missed extraordinary events at my children's schools or family functions. However, I had a village to help me. My mother and friends would help care for the children while I worked or attended school. A neighbor taught me how to meal prep for the week. Families at my children's school would take them to after-school activities, dedicated events, and sports. After getting out of work, I would then meet the children to ensure they participated with their peers. My employer would let me adjust my work schedule to accommodate my family and school life. Building a village is vital to taking the first step into nursing and overcoming obstacles. Overcoming these barriers and challenges has prepared me for the future. I have goals and dreams that need fulfillment throughout my lifetime.

Why nursing? What do I love about nursing? I love nursing because it allows me to be humble and to provide care, hope, and love to people. One gesture of kindness goes a long way in life. Everyone deserves to live healthily, to be happy, and to be part of solving the health issues we face in our communities, populations, and world. Being able to make a difference one person at a time is rewarding. It allows me to improve myself to make a difference in others.

Completing a surveillance of the number of Latina nurses in my community was shocking. Outpatient clinics, specialty clinics, emergency rooms, and schools need Latina nurses. The lack of Latina nurses contributes to the inequities and disparities seen in the Latino community. The care provided to the population could be better.

The scarcity of Spanish-speaking nurses make caring for the Latino community challenging. These challenges include transportation, education, and financial issues. Recruitment and retention could be better supported as precepting nurses experience burnout, and unfair wages.

Impacting my community as a nurse is essential to me. Throughout my nursing career, I have educated prospective students and new nurses about the culture and needs of the population. I have recruited Latina nurses to participate in free health and wellness fairs throughout my community. These fairs include blood pressure and diabetes checks, education, and providing available resources. I mentor and encourage Latinas to continue their nursing career after they have become a Certified Nursing Assistant (CNA) or License Practical Nurse (LPN). Precepting Latina nursing students as their instructors allows me to be a role model by sharing my stories of struggle, success, and accomplishments. It lets them know that they are not alone and that, as a community, we can contribute, help each other, and be effective in someone's life.

Latinas are helping to shape the future of nursing. They are rallying at the state and federal levels to make changes in the care of the population. The Latinas are forming and joining nursing associations and unions to improve the work environment and services in the community. Improving these issues in the community will open doors for individuals interested in getting into nursing and medicine. It provides the opportunity to see the problems, how they are being addressed, and what can be done about them. Demonstrations of positive and immense value will continue to encourage the next generation, hoping to make a difference in the population and community.

What is the most valuable lesson I have learned thus in my life? The most valuable lesson that I have learned in life is that perseverance and dedication to your goal or goals are critical to your success and happiness. Reaching those goals requires believing you can achieve and sustain anything. You must love yourself without prejudice, guilt, and limits. Building a support team or a village that can be on your side through your failures, accomplishments, and successes is crucial to reaching your goals. Sometimes, you are still determining where you are heading; however, no matter which path you take or how long it takes, you will reach the end of your journey.

My aspiration for my future in nursing is to continue my education. I am enrolled in a Doctor of Public Health program at Walden University. I will use my degree by getting involved in the state and local public health departments or nonprofit organizations to assist nursing in addressing the health disparities, inequities, and concerns in the Latino community and population. I envision a larger scale of Latina nurses joining forces to make changes, improvements, and a healthy environment for the Latino community.

FAVORITE NURSING MEMORY

When I was working in an inpatient hospice department, I had a patient who was terminally ill with stage four breast cancer. She had completed several rounds of chemotherapy, which only slowed the cancer down. The patient decided to stop all treatments and live life out for as long as she could. Her only adult child was on active military duty overseas. The daughter was notified of her mother's condition. She requested time to travel to be on her mother's side. In the meantime, the patient asked me to be at her bedside when she passed because she did not want to die alone. I complied and stayed beside her, playing the patient's favorite music. I held her hand until she passed. The daughter did not make it in time for her mother's passing. Knowing that the patient did not die alone brought comfort to the daughter. The daughter hugged me and thanked me for being beside her mother. This experience made me understand that nursing is about providing care and comfort to those in need.

BIOGRAPHY

Carmen Roman is married and is a mother to three adult children. She has three grandsons. Carmen is fluent in Spanish and English. She enjoys reading, writing, and spending time with her black lab, Tiki. Carmen enjoys entertaining at her home with her friends and family. She is an enthusiastic, caring, full of energy, bubbly, and loving individual.

Carmen has been in the nursing field since an early age. Carmen continues to be a lifetime learning student pursuing her doctor of public health at Walden University. She is employed as a didactic instructor for Licensed Practical Nursing (LPN) students. Carmen works as a school nurse at Capitol Region Education Council (CREC), an inner-city magnet school. She is the vice president of the Capitol Region Education Council (CREC) Health Professional Union at CREC in Hartford, Connecticut.

Carmen is very enthusiastic about volunteering on medical missions. She has volunteered on many medical missions to third-world countries for the past fifteen years. She aims to love and alleviate individuals suffering from diseases, poverty, and depression with medical/dental care, nutrition, water, and spiritual healing. Carmen volunteers at Lincoln Tech School's Lincoln Lends a Hand food pantry in New Britain, Connecticut, and also raises money for charities.

Carmen enjoys exploring and experiencing different countries. She travels about three to five times a year. She has traveled to Columbia, Nicaragua, El Salvador, Guatemala, and Mexico. She enjoys the food, music, culture, and the people.

Carmen Roman, MSN, RN
Carmenroman72@yahoo.com
LinkedIn: Carmen Roman

THE GÓMEZ EYES

NICOLE GÓMEZ

"I never imagined I would be a professor of nursing."

CURRENT POSITION

I am an assistant professor of nursing at a community college in Connecticut.

WHAT I LOVE ABOUT NURSING

I have worked in many settings that have had glaring disparity outcomes. I have worked over the years to address health disparities and increase minority nurses' access, funding, and awareness. As a nursing instructor, I am overwhelmed when I see previous students excelling and encouraging others into the field or along their nursing school journey. These types of full circle moments keep me motivated to continue to fight the good fight. Since then, so many beautiful connections have been made. I continue to see the good going around and try to be a part of the change that is needed as a nurse. I am committed to minority nursing student success. Being there for those whose shoes I once wore is a fulfilling achievement.

EYES TOWARD THE FUTURE

I know my eyes are BIG, BROWN and ROUND. In my family, they are the one thing that identifies you with our bloodline. These eyes are able to invite you in the door or kick you out! I can't tell you when I grew into them but I know my eyes have welcomed strangers to ask for help and reminded others to reconsider their statements.

I inherited my eyes from my father, Manuel Gómez Gonzalez Lopez Hernandez. Yes, these are all our family's names from grandparents down. I used to think my dad was joking when he said these names; but now I know they are my ancestors' names. Growing up in East Hartford, Connecticut, I didn't notice my name was different from other children's names and, in the last five years, I learned my last name has an accent! All these years I have been writing without one. I don't speak Spanish well and my dancing skills are minimal at best. I have had to explain often that my mom who raised me is white American and my dad is from Gurabo, Puerto Rico. I did not grow up speaking Spanish and had a difficult time feeling like I belonged. I was too Puerto Rican for the white girls and too white for the Puerto Rican girls. I hated the boxes that made me pick my mom's race or my dad's race, because there was not an option for both. This made me feel like a traitor. I carried the Latinx last name and the big brown eyes but the rest of me was a question mark.

During a trip to Puerto Rico when I was seventeen, I finally realized how much I have "the Gómez eyes." I was in a store in Gurabo, where my family is from, and a stranger asked me if I was a Gómez. I wasn't sure how they knew, but they pointed to my eyes and it appeared to be a dead giveaway. I found myself looking at all the beautiful colors and people around me knowing my blood is from the island. This connection is evident when I spend time with my Tia's, the laughter they have, the hugs they give and the kindness in their eyes, which match mine. We may miss each other's words, but the love is there. I can't translate that. I can only feel it. I always knew my dad, sisters, and I were affectionate and emotional but not until I was around my family in Puerto Rico did I really understand it is who we are. Caregiving is natural from babies to our elders. So, why are there not more Latinx nurses? I considered maybe many are caring for their families and do not explore this career field enough.

I never thought I would be going to college. In my family the goal was to get a "good job." My parents and siblings did not go to college; so, I wasn't expected to score high on SATs or attend a university. The pressure was not there. When I was a little girl, my cousin had a brain tumor as a baby, which left him deaf and blind. I will never forget his home care nurse. She cared for my family; she was an angel. I was five years old and the nurse explained to me and my cousins that we could play with our little cousin just like we played with other babies and children. She taught us to incorporate him as if he was able to see and hear everything we were doing. So, my perception of a nurse was as a unifier. Later, as a teenager my grandmother, whom lived with us, became sick. I wanted to help her in any way that I could and I started to care for her colostomy. This kind of caregiver role came naturally. I found out I wasn't grossed out when it came to bodily functions and started to consider nursing as a profession.

During a health careers class, a previous student, who became a phlebotomist, talked to our class. She explained how she had a car and an apartment and she was able to go on trips. This visual of someone like me, opened my eyes to the possibility that I could attend training or possibly college. When it came time to start applying for school, I was told college may not be an option since I was unable to take my SATs because I did not take the minimal math course. I asked about a community college in Queens, New York, where I had family and took a chance to apply. I was accepted! I couldn't believe I, yes, me Nicole, whose father completed grade school and my mother earned her GED. I wanted to move to New York so I could be around people from all over the world. My college was as diverse as you can imagine, and I was in my glory.

I started to take remedial classes at the community college, this means there are classes you take and pay for but not receive any credit. I remember being frustrated that I did not get to take these classes in high school and felt like this was slowing me down and making my two-year school turn into a three-year school. Nursing school was the most intense challenge of my life. I doubted myself each semester. Was I smart enough, capable enough, or committed enough? I had a core group of friends that pushed each other along the way. I was often told I spent too much time talking to patients, as if this was the worst thing I could do. I enjoyed hearing their stories and understanding their disease. I was so discouraged and wondered to myself how is this a compassionate career when all the teachers intimidate you and make you feel like you are incapable. I know it does not have to be this way and wanted to show them that I would be a nurse. I finished the program and received an Associate's Degree of Applied Sciences in Nursing. Shortly after, I started my career as a Registered Nurse (RN).

I began my nursing career when I was twenty-one years old, at a local hospital in our state's capital. This environment reminded me of New York. I remember interviewing and, when they asked me what I was looking for, I remember saying diversity of staff and patients. I landed the best position on a unit that had staff from various countries who spoke multiple languages. I felt at home. My nurse manager was Jamaican American and she encouraged everyone to go back to school and continue our education. My work mom and mentor could see the passion in my eyes for patients and families. I cared for them as if they were my family members. Yes, these Gómez eyes are windows into my heart, they are genuine and authentic . . . unless of course you see the irritation I feel when I see unequal treatment of my family, friends, loved ones, or patients. I know the racism that exists, in nursing and in nursing education, and will continue to work on addressing what I see . . . the inequalities, the misconceptions, and the unethical treatment that continues.

LET THE EYES SHOW YOU

I struggle when I get so frustrated. My eyes become bigger and, sometimes, I roll my eyes out of irritation. Oftentimes, my emotions take over and I am unable to hide my disgust. I am learning the skills to get my point across and take the emotion out; but the Latina side of me is infuriated and, morally, I don't understand how else to say it.

Whenever I am doubted or dismissed, it fuels me to do better, and have the "I will show you" mentality. The funny part is, nobody is daring me. I am daring myself to show them who Yes, I am Nicole Gómez Gonzalez Lopez Hernandez, half Puerto Rican, MSN, RN.

My biggest obstacle as a nurse has been feeling like an imposter. I would often see nurse leaders who do not look, sound, or act like me. I never imagined I would be a Professor of nursing. Who do I think I am? One day, I fear someone will point me out in a crowd and embarrass me, finally telling the world that I am not who I say I am and need to sit down. I am learning to ignore these thoughts and I have started to think . . . Why not me? I have more than twenty years of nursing experience and a Master's Degree. I love being a nurse. I definitely have room to improve, but I am a work in progress. Even for this story, I wondered to myself, "Am I Latina enough? Am I worthy of sharing my nursing story?" Yes, let "the Gómez eyes" show you. I am enough and worthy of telling my story.

FAVORITE NURSING MEMORY

I continued on for my Bachelor's Degree from Sacred Heart University in Fairfield, Connecticut, and my Masters in Science in Nursing (MSN) from the University of Hartford. During a class in professional nursing organizations, I noticed that all the nurses on the panel were white. It triggered a thought for me. Were there any Latinx nursing organizations? I asked one of my professors this question and they were able to share the National Association of Hispanic Nurses (NAHN). I lived in Connecticut; there was not a local chapter. So, I decided to reach out to the national folks to see what this would entail. I was told there was a chapter years before, but it closed. If I wanted, I could start a new chapter with three other people.

This is when history happened. Myself along with three other Latinx nurses began the NAHN Connecticut chapter in 2010. In 2011, I was tired of driving across the state and decided we should make another local chapter closer to my home NAHN-Hartford chapter. A second chapter was born. These two new endeavors worked on helping the local community while uniting nurses and created a network of Latinx nurses who wanted to excel. This was my biggest contribution to the nursing profession.

BIOGRAPHY

Nicole Gómez, MSN, RN, has been a nurse for more than twenty years and loves being a part of a community that cares about the wellness of others. She's currently an Assistant Professor of nursing at Capital Community College and enjoys every minute of seeing her students excel. She Co-founded a minority nursing mentorship club for nursing students to be mentored while they finish their last year of nursing school. Chelsea Rojas, was one of the mentees and Tina Loarte-Rodriguez was her mentor. Nicole loves to travel to experience different cultures and finds excitement in tasting great food, of course. Friends and family are a big part of her life and she always makes time to share laughter with those she loves. Nicole has a ten-year-old son, and she always tries to impress him with her ideas. Her step-daughters are always there to back her up. Her mother is her biggest cheerleader and supporter. When she's alone, she's usually listening to music, spending time with her faith, or exploring a good podcast. Nicole is a dog lover and appreciates taking her dog for a walk in nature. She chases rainbows on cloudy days and always makes sure to take a moment to appreciate and to share the little things in life that bring her joy.

Nicole Gómez, MSN, RN
NicoleGomezRN@gmail.com

BROTHER'S ILLNESS LEADS TO REWARDING CAREER

MARTHA SALMON

"The best view comes after the hardest climb."

CURRENT POSITION

I am a professor at a university in Los Angeles, California and a pediatric travel nurse.

WHAT I LOVE ABOUT NURSING

I love all the lives I am lucky enough to be a part of and hopefully make an impact on.

PATH TO NURSING COMES FULL CIRCLE

If someone would have told me years ago that I would be sitting here as a mastered-prepared nurse, teaching for a university in Los Angeles, California and contemplating going back to school for my doctor in nursing practice (DNP), I would have laughed. How did I do it? How did this first-time Latina college student do it? Let's go back to the beginning.

The year is 2000. I am twelve years old and my little brother, the youngest of us three, only two years old, has been sick for over a week. Vomiting, pale and super lethargic. My mom, younger sister, and I begin to worry. My mom informs my sister and I that she will be taking our brother to see his doctor so we will be staying at our babysitter's house later than usual. We finish our day at school, we arrive at our babysitter's house as usual, and 5 p.m. hits. I know my mom said we were going to stay later than usual, but a part of me had hopes that she would still pick us up on time. Six o'clock . . . seven o'clock, now I am starting to worry. What is taking so long? My babysitter's phone rings, my heart and my tummy feel funny. This can't be good. The babysitter hangs up and she locks eyes with me. She sees the worry in my face. She pulls my sister and I together and crouches low to get on our eye level.

"Girls, you'll be sleeping over tonight . . . your brother is very sick," she says.

"What is wrong with him? Why can't we see him? Why can't my mom pick us up?" I ask, trying to hold back tears as to not scare my little sister.

"The doctors want to run more tests on your brother, so your mom has to stay with him. She will come get you as soon as she can."

I lost it. What can be going on? How sick is he? I can't tell you details to fill the next couple days. But they were probably the longest days I had ever had as a twelve-year-old. We get picked up from school by our babysitter and she tells us we are going to stay one more night. I feel sick. What is going on?

We get to her house and she finally says, "I have to tell you girls something." My sister and I sit up eagerly, just waiting for more information. Our babysitter proceeds to tell us that mom called and informed her that my brother has cancer. I don't even fully understand what that means but my heart breaks and the tears flow down my face uncontrollably. I want my mom. I want to see my brother.

After that initial shock and maybe a couple more days, my mom finally picks us up. She apologizes for being away so long and fills us in on what's going on. We find out that my brother has been and is still admitted at the Children's Hospital of Los Angeles because he has something called Wilms tumor. From that moment, we spent three months in and out of that hospital. Many different people come in and out of my brother's room. But the people who made the biggest impression, and the ones I remembered the most, were the nurses.

Fast forward to 2005, I am a junior in high school and I have no idea what I want to do with my life. My dad immigrated from Nicaragua and had made a great living for himself running his own business, but I knew that wasn't for me. I start to ask my grandparents what they suggest. Being older Hispanics all they say is "Marty, you just need to graduate high school and get a 'good job,' like working at a bank, or something." College was not something they ever talked about, but I knew I had to do more. I had no real guidance when it came to college or education after high school. So by the end of my senior year, I started really thinking. I enrolled in my local community college and started taking my general education classes. Things are going well, and when I think about what I am good at, I remember the nurses at Children's Hospital Los Angeles. I think, "The nurses always looked so happy. They were so kind to my brother and me. They gave medications. I don't think the job looked that 'hard' and I like helping people." I started looking into how to becoming a nurse. I come across a for-profit school and go to their information session. I am eighteen years old. Not knowing anything about college, the school tells me, "In order to become a registered nurse (RN), you have to do this program first; you will become a licensed vocational nurse. Then you can go back to school to become a registered nurse." It's April 2007, I sign my name on what seems like a thousand forms and start my one-year journey to becoming a licensed vocational nurse (LVN). The year flew by, I learned so much and am so excited to graduate. It is now April 2008, and I walk across the stage to receive my certificate of completion... seven months pregnant. I am nineteen, done with LVN school, and about to have a newborn. I thought by having a child, working as a LVN is where my journey had to end. I didn't mind, though. Afterall, I was going to "have a good job," like my grandparents always told me.

I took nine months to raise my daughter before I started looking for jobs. During my time off, I was taking general education classes at my local community college. When it came to looking for work, to my surprise, I didn't find much. So I started working as a home health LVN for children. I would make home visits, provide the necessary care, and do paper charting. It paid the bills but I knew I wanted more, especially because I was pregnant with my second child. I see an opening for an LVN at none other than Children's Hospital Los Angeles (CHLA). I remember thinking, "Can you imagine, working at the hospital where my brother was cared for?" I go for my interview and I am in awe of how beautiful the hospital was. It looked exactly the same as I remembered all those years ago. I admit I had a bit of imposter syndrome and thought, "Why would they choose me? I don't even have hospital experience." I leave the interview feeling hopeful but expecting the worst. About one week later, I get the call, "We'd like to offer you the position for LVN on 6 North Rehab." I cried. I was so happy to be working in a hospital, making more money and giving back to the hospital that saved my brother's life!

It took a couple months of me working as an LVN at Children's Hospital to realize that I wanted even more. I wanted to be an RN at CHLA. I soon enrolled back into my local community college and started chipping away at my prerequisites to get into an RN program. It took me a total of five years to finish all my prerequisites, and I was finally accepted into Citrus College's LVN to RN program. It was a one-year program and I was luckily still able to work full time. There I was: twenty-five years old, with two kids ages four and two, a husband, working full time and going to school full time. To say it was the hardest year of my life would be an understatement. So many sleepless nights, so many tears, but also so many great memories, and a true test to how strong a person needs to be when they are determined.

In 2013, I graduated with my associate degree in nursing (ADN). It was one of the best days of my life, next to the birth of my kids and my wedding day, of course. But the journey wasn't over yet. I had to pass the National Council Licensure Examination (NCLEX-RN®). I studied for about two months before I took the test. The test took me the whole six hours and I ran out of time. I was on number 200-something, when the clock hit six hours and computer screen turned black. I started bawling, there was no way I passed. I left the testing center feeling defeated and embarrassed. I get home and I decide to try "the trick." All nurses know exactly what this means. I registered to take the NCLEX again, and it wouldn't let me schedule a test date! I knew not to get my hopes up too high but it was hard not to. Three days later I called the Board of Registered Nursing (BRN) to get my results and the sweet lady on the phone said "I can't tell you if you passed or not yet. You'll have to wait for the official results, But I will say you can celebrate with your family tonight." I PASSED MY NCLEX®! I AM OFFICIALLY A REGISTERED NURSE. I DID IT. WE DID IT.

I get right to work on my Bachelor of Science in Nursing (BSN). I only had my ADN so I know my options are limited. My first RN position was at a dialysis center; I worked there for one year. I worked on an adult medical surgical floor, too; and I finally obtained my BSN. And where do I apply? That's right, CHLA. It's 2015 and I am back to where it all started. My years at CHLA flew by. I made the best of friends and learned so much. I have taken care of so many patients, and really grew into who I am supposed to be as a nurse and as a person. Working with so many different people, I found myself always so happy to see a fellow Latino nurse. I started to look into statistics, because reality was, there wasn't that many Latino nurses. We were certified nurse assistants (CNA), we were housekeepers, but why aren't there more nurses? It came to me that I should create a safe place, a community rather, for Latinos in nursing.

Creating a community took a lot of thought and a lot of trial and error. But finally, Latina, RN was born. I wanted something meaningful and a way to show off our pride to be Latinos in nursing. It started with just merchandise, shirts, stickers and bags. But it quickly turned into something much bigger. It is a way to network. It is a place to find mentors. It is a place to share your story, your journey to RN, in order to encourage and to inspire anyone who was in school to be a nurse or if someone thought of becoming a nurse. Through Latina, RN, now called Latinx, RN, I have been able to reach so many people, I have been able to experience the most amazing things, such as traveling to speak to a room full of nurses and nursing students, being the face of a big scrub company as they donated to a large Latino nursing organization, and speaking for organizations, such as AltaMed and USC. I was able to do a medical mission in Uganda. I have done two commercials, one for Mucinex and the other for WSSxReebok highlighting the importance of Latinx, RN. In the middle of all these incredible opportunities I've been a part of, I graduated with my Masters in Nursing and am now teaching at UCLA. I have truly found a passion for teaching.

I share my story not to boast, but to encourage and to inspire those who want more. I was a pregnant teenager who really didn't know what I was getting myself into. I shouldn't be where I am now. But with hard work, faith and the support from your loved ones, ANYTHING IS POSSIBLE.

Si yo puedo hacerlo cualquiera puede hacerlo. I'll leave you with my favorite quote, that helped get me through some tough times: "The best view comes after the hardest climb."

FAVORITE NURSING MEMORY

When I think of my favorite nursing memory, the year 2017 easily comes to mind. I had been taking care of a chronically ill and "frequent flyer" patient for some time. She was a four-year-old girl with the biggest personality. The month was October, near Halloween, and everyone would ask what she wanted to be for Halloween. Her response was always the same. "I want to be Nurse Marfa" (She couldn't pronounce "th" in Martha.) Everyone laughed it off. But come Halloween, this child bought a purple top that was an exact replica of one that I owned, black scrub pants and a pink headband in her hair, just like I always wore to work. Everyone on the unit got involved and even made her a Nurse Marfa badge. My heart still explodes thinking of this memory. This child, for whatever reason, loved me and wanted to be like me. It is a constant reminder on how your patients are always watching you and learning from you even if you don't feel like they are. You're making an impact on someone's life every day, at all times.

BIOGRAPHY

Martha Salmon lives in Southern California with her two kids, husband and puppy. She currently teaches at UCLA with intentions to go back to school for her doctor of nursing practice (DNP) degree soon. She still runs Latinx, RN part time but hopes to put more time into the business once she's done with school.

Martha Salmon, MSN, RN, CPN
latinarnofficial@gmail.com
IG: @marthareysalmon

DON'T GIVE UP

SHARON RAMIREZ

"Don't give up or allow the obstacles and challenges you face to deter you from accomplishing your goal."

CURRENT POSITION

I am a director of nursing at a outpatient endoscopy center in the Fort Lauderdale area.

WHAT I LOVE ABOUT NURSING

As I reflect on the journey I have traveled throughout my nursing career, what I appreciate and love most about nursing are the endless opportunities it has provided me, to grow and learn, both personally and professionally. Improving the quality of the lives of my patients by advocating, educating, and empowering them is such a rewarding feeling. I consider it a privilege to have a patient place their trust in me as I help them navigate through their challenging health issues. My nursing career has allowed me to witness the moment of birth, as well as, the end of life. I feel an immense sense of pride to have such a meaningful career, and I am humbled to know that I make a positive difference in the lives of others.

NURSING WITH COMPASSION

Today, I am proud to fulfill my role as director of nursing at an outpatient endoscopy center in South Florida. I could not have conceived of achieving this position twenty-five years ago, when as a stay-at-home mom, I decided to take a few online courses to keep my mind busy. At that time, I spent my days taking care of my two young children and maintaining the home. Feeling restless, I enrolled in an online program offered through a local community college. I had no specific career goal, I just needed to do something to challenge and stimulate my mind. I only registered for one class at a time, and sometimes I skipped a few semesters, depending on how busy the children's school schedules were in that quarter. It wasn't until several years later that I decided to pursue a nursing career. It was then that I started taking my coursework serious and focused on completing the necessary prerequisite courses to qualify for a nursing program. Ultimately, it took me eight years to complete the required coursework necessary to register for the Bachelor of Science in Nursing (BSN) degree program.

Initially, I struggled with my decision to pursue the academic endeavor of earning my BSN. I was filled with self-doubt. I was intimidated by the challenges I faced as a student, committing myself to a difficult and intense program at the age of thirty-seven. However, I knew it was necessary, as I was contending with a marital separation and needed to acquire skills that would allow me to work to support my children and myself. I relocated from Arizona to Florida to be closer to my family and began my new academic program.

Upon starting my classes, I realized I was finding it harder to learn. I wasn't processing the content as easily as I did when I was younger. It was taking me longer to fully comprehend the material, requiring me to spend more time studying just to keep up with the coursework. There were several times I wanted to give up. Many nights I stayed up late, crying and feeling frustrated because I was overwhelmed. I was doubting myself, questioning if I made the right decision to take on such a huge challenge at my age. I could have easily taken an office job to earn a paycheck, but I knew I wanted a career. Each time those negative doubts infiltrated my mind, I countered them with determination. I did not want to fail. I reminded myself that through my actions, I was setting an example for my children. I was teaching them the invaluable lesson of determination and honoring our commitments. I wanted to show them that giving up is not an option just because there are obstacles in the way. So, on those nights, when I thought I couldn't continue, I'd wipe the tears and keep going. Ultimately, at almost forty years old, I finished the program at the top of my class, and I earned my degree with honors.

After passing the National Council Licensure Examination–Registered Nurses (NCLEX-RN®), I was offered my first nursing position as a bedside RN on a med/surg/oncology unit. Initially, I was disappointed with the position because throughout nursing school, I really desired to start my career as an emergency room (ER) RN. However, looking back now, I am so grateful for the experience of working on that unit. Although the twelve-hour shifts were physically and mentally challenging, providing care to the oncology patients has been the most gratifying experience I've had in my nursing career thus far. It was through my work on that unit that I learned what it really meant to be a nurse. I developed true compassion and empathy for the suffering my patients endured. I realized what a privilege it is to take care of people when they are the most vulnerable, scared, and in pain.

Many of those patients spent weeks and sometimes months with us in the hospital. The nursing staff developed close relationships with the patients and their families. This made it that much more difficult to deal with the loss when, unfortunately, some of them inevitably passed away. Many times, we attended their funerals and over time, it became emotionally taxing when one of them would succumb to their illness.

One particular experience stands out in my mind. We had a patient who had been with us for several months and was declining rapidly. We knew she didn't have much time left. One day when I arrived at work, I was assigned to be her nurse. Based on her clinical status, we knew it was very likely she was going to pass away during my shift. That was something I needed to prepare myself for because knowing you are going to lose a patient while in your care, even though it is expected, is emotionally difficult. Her two adult sons and a daughter-in-law were at her bedside throughout the day. I entered her room often to check on her family as they stood vigil at her side. During one of my check-ins, I noticed her breathing had changed, it was shallow and slow, we knew the end was near. I waited with her family and shortly after, she took her last breath. The family was understandably devastated, however, despite their immense grief, they took the time to express their gratitude for the care I provided to their loved one.

A few days later, after our shift, a patient care assistant and I left work together and went to the funeral home to attend the patient's wake and to pay our respects. This was commonly something we did if we had developed a close bond to the patient. When we arrived, we were so impressed by how many people were in attendance. The funeral home had to open two rooms to accommodate the attendees. We remained in the back of the room, as her son was in the middle of delivering the eulogy and we did not want to cause a disruption. Additionally, since we drove straight from work, we were still dressed in our scrubs, which made us uncomfortable. We intended to wait until he finished so we could pay our respects to the family and leave, however, when he noticed us standing in the back of the room, he stopped speaking. He walked down the center aisle, directly towards us. He took us each by the hand and walked us to the front of the room and sat us in the front row with the family. He then returned to the podium and proceeded to tell everyone that we were considered part of the family because of the care we provided to his mother until the end.

That experience is my proudest nursing moment. I was so honored and moved by the way we were embraced by the family. The respect and gratitude they showed for the work we did and the care we provided to their family member validated my decision to become a nurse. That experience was a defining moment for me. It helped form the foundation of my nursing career, and solidified my commitment to always provide clinical care with compassion, empathy, and respect.

Since my time as a new nurse just starting out, I have built a successful and gratifying career. I'm grateful for the ongoing journey of learning and growing I've experienced with each new role I have filled. I've enjoyed many opportunities to explore various avenues of nursing, which have included both in-patient and out-patient services. Ultimately, I was drawn to the surgical environment and have spent the last eleven years in the operating room (OR) setting.

As I moved throughout my career, I unfortunately did encounter instances of bullying and harsh judgements, not just towards myself, but to others, especially towards the newer nurses. It saddened me to watch professionals in a vocation that is committed to caring for the sick with compassion and empathy, be so cruel and demeaning to their peers. I often found myself in a mentoring role, nurturing and teaching the newer team members.

Those efforts placed me on a path to roles in leadership. My first leadership position was as an OR assistant manager. Since then, I have worked as an interim director of surgical services at a local hospital, an administrator at an outpatient surgery center, and currently, as director of nursing at an outpatient endoscopy center. These roles have afforded me the opportunity to help empower and support the next generation of nurses, which gives me purpose and personal fulfillment.

My advice to anyone who wants to start a nursing career but is doubting themselves, don't be intimidated. Be tenacious.

Don't give up or allow the obstacles and challenges you face to deter you from accomplishing your goal. The nursing field is fluid and provides endless opportunities for personal and professional development. Your determination will provide you with a gratifying and rewarding career.

FAVORITE NURSING MEMORY

My favorite nursing memory took place in the operating room, when I was working at an outpatient surgical center. My patient was a very elderly man. He was extremely nervous to be put to sleep with anesthesia. As we were wheeling him into the OR, he looked up at me and asked in a timid, childlike voice, "Will you please hold my hand?" I took his hand in mine and didn't let go until he was asleep. After his procedure, I held his hand as he woke from the anesthesia. As he slowly regained consciousness, he looked down at his hand and saw that I was still holding it, then he smiled and said, "Thank you." I'll never forget the look in his eyes as he entrusted me, a complete stranger to him, to provide a sense of safety and security, when he was most vulnerable.

BIOGRAPHY

Sharon Ramirez is a Latina of Mexican and Puerto Rican descent. She was born and raised in the Bronx, a borough of New York City. She currently resides in South Florida, where she has lived for the last eighteen years. Her career spans fifteen years and includes experience in bedside nursing, oncology, pain management, and in-patient and out-patient surgical services. She earned her BSN degree from Nova Southeastern University, as well as a Master of Science in Nursing (MSN), with a focus in clinical informatics from Grand Canyon University in Phoenix, Arizona. She currently works as a Director of Nursing at an outpatient endoscopy center in the Fort Lauderdale area. Sharon is an empty nester with three adult children. She enjoys traveling to visit them when her schedule allows. She has two extremely spoiled Yorkies, which occupy her time and keep her busy. In her spare time, Sharon enjoys gardening, which she finds gratifying and relaxing.

Sharon Ramirez, MSN, RN

Sramirez.rn@gmail.com

NOT LIKE THE REST OF THEM? HOW I BECAME A CONFIDENT, PROUD LATINA NURSE

JENIFFER DOLINTA

"Be bold. Be fearless. You are enough."

CURRENT POSITION

I am a clinical educator in a rural hospital and a university graduate research assistant while completing my doctoral degree.

WHAT I LOVE ABOUT NURSING

I love the various paths in which nurses at different levels can impact patient care. No matter their role, nurses make a difference. I am a Latina nurse. I am proud of who I am, caring, driven, educated, and resilient. As you read both of these sentences, you probably think those are words spoken by someone confident in who they are as a person and professional. If you were to have met me almost twelve years ago, newly graduated from nursing school, you would have encountered a young woman full of fear. I was afraid of being judged, being rejected, and being a failure. I felt an overwhelming need to work harder and to prove that I belonged there. Navigating the nursing profession as a Latina has taught me some tough and, at times, painful lessons. But it also has taught me the power of perseverance. It has taught me that my voice matters, my ideas are valuable, and risks are worth taking.

'YOU ARE NOT LIKE THE REST OF THEM'

My mother and I immigrated to the United States from El Salvador when I was five years old. While many kindergarteners were working on their numbers, alphabet, and drawing skills, I was learning English. From very early on, I can remember feeling excluded and separated from my peers, having to be taken away every day to attend the "special" class, English as a Second Language (ESL). Living in an area with few minority families, there were not many other students in the same situation as myself. I hated it. As one of the few Hispanic girls at my school, all I wanted was to fit in. As young as I was, this was the beginning of my constant desire to prove that I could be "one of them." I was not only going to perfect my English, but I was going to be engulfed in American culture. Little did I know that I was losing a part of what made me, me. Fast forward to hearing the phrase, "You are not like the rest of them," for the first time. My family had moved from Virginia to Texas, where I was attending a school with predominantly Hispanic students for the first time. I was fifteen years old, interviewing for an officer position on my high school dance team. In my panel interview were a few of the moms that would be helping to select the ranking of the candidates. After asking me the standard panel questions "What do you plan to do for the team?" and "Why do you think you would make a good officer?" one of the moms said, "You are so well-spoken. You are not like the rest of them." At that moment, I was speechless. I thought, OK, I did it; I have fixed one of my flaws. Yet, what she said didn't feel like a compliment. I was being excluded again, but in a much different way. The "them" that she was referring to were other Hispanic girls. I tucked that away, thanked her for her comment, and left.

A few years later, I received a scholarship award from a local nonprofit group as an undergraduate nursing student. Only two of us in our entire nursing class were selected, both minorities. Being the first in my family to attend college, I was honored and proud to be recognized for my hard work and academic achievements. We were invited to attend a luncheon with the group's scholarship committee as part of the award. I planned my outfit for days; I was so excited to attend this event. The day came, and we met one of our university professors so she could drive us.

It is hard to find the words to describe this place; I had never been somewhere so elegant before. Everything was precisely in its place, pressed white tablecloths with matching napkins, delicate China dishes with little pink flowers and matching tea sets, rows of forks, spoons, and knives all carefully laid out. I quickly noticed that my classmate and I were the only two women of color in the room. Although I was used to this at this point, I felt uneasy about it. As we sat down and started to chat, the ladies were eager to learn about us. The longer the conversations went, the more I squirmed in my chair. Although I genuinely believe they perceived it as a compliment, what I heard was their surprised comments, "You are so well dressed," "You have such great manners," "You are so well spoken," "Look at your posture. I am impressed," and the dreaded "You are different." To say I felt as if I was on display is an understatement; I felt insignificant. By the time we left, I don't think I said more than a few words on the drive back to school. I started to ask myself why I was perceived as different from other Hispanic women. Why is it considered a compliment? And why do I feel so terrible every time I hear that phrase?

When I entered the nursing profession, I began working in a progressive care unit, where I was paired with the only other Latina nurse on the floor as my preceptor. I didn't know it then, but she would play a significant role in my journey. Though she was just a few years older than me, she seemed to have so much confidence in embracing her identity as a Mexican American. She was strong in advocating for Hispanic patients ensuring that they were receiving quality care and translation services were easily accessible on the unit. Up to this point, I had found that if I put my Hispanic identity aside, I was more accepted by other non-minority nurses and leaders. It wasn't that I was ashamed of my ethnicity; rather, it wasn't something I openly discussed. I just wanted to keep my head down and move forward. Here she was, not shying away from who she was. I felt that I could be myself for the first time and not be seen "as different." Her support for the first few years of my nursing career opened my eyes to the significance of having mentors, preceptors, and role models that share your experiences, look like you, and provide comfort in a profession where less than 10 percent of nurses are Hispanic. The "them" I had been avoiding was where I wanted to belong and felt most at home.

Over the next few years, I continued to want to capture that sense of belonging, to have someone take me under their wing, and to guide me. Although I didn't find the level of support I sought, I was fortunate to find leaders and peers who "saw something in me" and encouraged me to pursue higher education and career advancement. In 2014, I decided that I wanted to better prepare myself to be that person for others and chose to pursue a Master's Degree in Nursing Education. I enjoyed teaching, but what I found brought me the greatest sense of accomplishment was being able to mentor other nurses and techs in their professional journeys. I took a leap and began a path as a nurse educator.

After completing my Master's Degree, I felt the need to further my education and pursue a Doctor of Philosophy (PhD) in Nursing. At this point in my career, I felt as if something was missing, and I hadn't fully captured my authentic purpose in nursing; I hoped to capture that in pursuit of my Doctoral Degree. In applying for a doctoral program, I wrote about my desire to study cardiac resuscitation. Although this is an important area of research and something I was very involved in, it was not my passion. I have always been interested in the impact of diversity in nursing and healthcare delivery, having experienced it firsthand. But I didn't want to pursue this topic for fear of it being rejected or being seen as less valuable than the research of my peers. Although I was actively involved in the Hispanic nurses association and sat on a leadership council for health equity in my community, I stayed away from pursuing this topic for the first two years of my nursing PhD journey. I just couldn't find it in myself to go there. I was blessed in my career to find the right people when I most needed them, and they gave me the courage to take that next step. One of my professors, whom I would call a mentor, role model, and friend, gave me the strength to find my voice and pursue my research on the experiences of Hispanic nurse leaders. Since working on my study, I have met powerful Hispanic female nurse leaders, heard their stories, and shared in their laughter and tears. I have learned that my identity as a Hispanic woman is integral to my role as a nurse, a scholar, and a leader. It is not something to shy away from but rather embrace. I AM one of them, strong, resilient, and perseverant. It wasn't until I found my voice as a Latina in nursing that I found the strength in the community I had always been searching for. I hope to be that guiding light for others that question their sense of belonging and are afraid to see where their journeys may take them, just as others have been there for me.

FAVORITE NURSING MEMORY

In my first role as a Nurse Educator, I was the only minority nurse in the department. Although not significant in my workload and day-to-day tasks, I never realized how my career choice could impact other minority nurses. After teaching an electrocardiogram (EKG) class to a group of new graduate nurses, I vividly remember this young Hispanic nurse coming up to me and very shyly asking me what I had done to become an educator. As we sat and talked for a bit, she told me that she was the first person in her family to go to college, she had no Hispanic professors in nursing school, and I was the first Hispanic nurse she had encountered. She was open to asking me questions and, in the end, asked if it was OK if she reached out with questions or for advice. Her story resonated with mine. I have had many similar stories throughout my years as an educator, and I still keep in touch with many of these nurses. Having the privilege to share in their struggles and successes has been one of the most rewarding parts of my nursing career.

BIOGRAPHY

Jeniffer Dolinta, MS, RN, PCCN-K, NPD-BC, CNE, has been a registered nurse for eleven years. She immigrated as a young child from El Salvador to the United States with her mom, searching for a life with better opportunities. In high school, she became involved in HOSA- Future Health Professionals (formerly known as Health Occupations Students of America), where she was exposed to different healthcare roles. Through this experience, she chose to pursue a career in nursing. Jeniffer graduated from Texas Woman's University with a Bachelor of Science in Nursing, a Master of Science in Nursing Education, and is in the final stages of completing a PhD in nursing. Jeniffer began her nursing career in progressive care, where she found her passion for teaching and has worked in different nurse educator roles over the past seven years. She is a strong advocate for nursing professional development and nursing excellence and is board certified in progressive care nursing, nursing professional development, and as a certified nurse educator. Jeniffer believes that all nurses, regardless of their background or personal experiences, should have an equal opportunity to succeed in nursing. She is committed to recruiting, retaining, and growing the next generation of nurses. In her free time, Jeniffer enjoys exploring the Oregon outdoors with her husband and son.

She dedicates her story to her mother, who has been a pillar of strength, love, and support throughout her journey.

Jeniffer Dolinta, MS, RN, PCCN-K, NPD-BC, CNE
JenifferDolinta@gmail.com
LinkedIn: @jeniffer-dolinta

ENFERMERA DEL PUEBLO

ZACNITÉ VARGAS AVALOS

"When you say my name, you carry their stories, their pain, their fears, their loss, their triumphs, and everything in between."

CURRENT POSITION

I am a registered nurse and President and Founder of the National Association of Hispanic Nurses–Tennessee Chapter.

WHAT I LOVE ABOUT NURSING

I love nursing because it is a profession rooted in compassion that can lead to endless cycles of personal growth and career opportunities.

MY NAME IS . . .

It was a hot summer day in 2016, the first day of my junior year in nursing school, and my heart was racing. I wasn't nervous because it was the first day, I was nervous because I knew that what I was about to do was one of the last chains that held me hostage to assimilation. As the teacher made her way down the alphabetized class names, I could feel my heart pounding in the pit of my stomach, my palms became sweaty and I felt my face getting hotter and hotter.

Say it, say your name loud and proud. Enough is enough... Ms.... Zack...Umm...Ms. Zack...Ms. Vargas?

I am not sure if it was my adrenaline and anticipation of my name being called out incorrectly for the fifteenth school year in a row by tongues that could not bend and twist like mine. Or maybe it was the accumulated anger I kept shoving down into the crevices of my soul all summer long as anti-immigrant rhetoric lingered in the air. "*When Mexico sends its people, they're not sending their best . . . They're sending people that have lots of problems, and they're bringing those problems with us.*" The echoing of this phrase kept ringing in my ears over and over and over again. That wasn't me, and it sure as hell wasn't my community.

MS. VARGAS? ARE YOU HERE?

I felt my sweaty palms grip the edge of the table, my legs

slightly shaky. I cleared my throat and with the same strength my parents had to fabricate from their bodies when they crossed the Southern Mexican desert. I took a deep breath and said, "My name is Zacnité. It's pronounced Zac-ni-té." At that moment, the only thing I could think of was how proud I was of being a daughter of immigrants, a daughter to Soledad Avalos and Jesus Vargas, my pillars, my constant drumbeat, my foundation.

When you say my name, you carry their stories, their pain, their fears, their losses, their triumphs, and everything in between. I will continue to fight for them, for me, for us, and for every person that will come along to harvest from the seeds we've planted. I am not entirely sure what happened after that. I don't think I even remember what that day's lecturer was focused on. I had zoned out with memories of having to take responsibilities of an adult when I was a child, the immigration story I am reminded of every February 7. I sat there recalling all the discrimination and injustices inflicted on undocumented communities because of the lack of a nine-digit golden number defining your humanity in this country. I sat there looking around at a sea of white classmates. I was the only brown face reflecting my community.

I wonder what my life could have been like if my parents hadn't made this life-altering decision. But I am here. I am in a room full of people that don't look like me, don't speak like me. They can't comprehend the hopes and dreams I carry on my shoulder of those whose eyes have closed while crossing the desert for a better life, like my tia. May you rest in peace.

I am a nurse because my community depends on it. I do it for you, for families who fear deportation, for all the brown-skinned boys and girls who will come after me in hopes that when they do become the "first" in their families, we sustain them as they journey their own American dream.

SIN PAPELES Y SIEMPRE SIN MIEDO

My parents never shied away from talking to me about my undocumented status. If anything, that was the reason why I had to do so well in school, no chances for mistakes, no room for rest, always with a book in hand, keeping myself busy. I had always been an honor-roll student, getting academic recognition throughout my school years, and always getting the best feedback from my teachers, the typical "teacher's pet" scenario. It wasn't until my senior year of high school that I would be tasked with applying for as many scholarships as I was eligible for. I came back with an empty sheet in hand, a knot in my throat. Fighting back tears, I said, "I don't qualify for much . . . I'm not a citizen of the United States." I felt like the ground had swallowed me and that was the first time I remember feeling ashamed of being who I was. At that moment, I felt like I was never going to succeed in a country that did not accept my humanity. I came home crying to my mom, telling her I did not want to go to college anymore, and that there were no opportunities for me. She looked right into my eyes and said to me, "Tu si vas a ir a la universidad, por que nadie te va a poder quitarte tu educación." She was right, we were going to find a way to pay for school. That summer I became invested in advocating for students like me who didn't have a clear path to college because of our status.

Even before college, I knew that as a Latina, I needed to be a voice for my community. As an undocumented immigrant, I was forced to navigate through safety net clinics, public health departments, and whatever else was necessary to seek care for myself and my family. In 2012, after the Deferred Action and Childhood Arrival (DACA) program was announced, I joined the Tennessee Immigrant and Refugee Rights Coalition (TIRRC). I knew that my passion for justice was only going to get louder and louder. I became a lead organizer for immigration reform, including defending DACA at the US Supreme Court, leading the fight for tuition equality for Tennessee's undocumented youth, and leading the victory in 2022 for HB2309, legislation that expanded the eligibility for DACA recipients to obtain a professional or commercial license in Tennessee. Through it all, I had people who rooted for me, supported me, and never doubted my ability to lead. I knew that if I could fight for my humanity in this country, I could become the nurse my community needed.

After graduating from college with a Bachelor of Nursing in Science (BSN) degree, I began my nursing career as a Pediatric Nurse. Little did I know that this was the start of a career that would change my trajectory in life.

As much as I can try to articulate the life of a nurse, you aren't able to understand this profession until you become one. You'll be able to understand the depths of this profession when you embrace a child who is terminally ill, hold onto the hands of tearful parents praying for a miracle until you clock out with an empty belly because you were so busy that day you forgot to take a lunch break, or worse, you find yourself weeping in the corner of your bedroom thinking about what else you could have done to save that child. Being a pediatric nurse reminded me of how resilient we can all be. I took care of the sickest of the sick and yet these children had a light in their eyes that made me want to do more, to be more, to fight more. I loved my kiddos and I loved this career that let me love others, but it still did not feel like I was doing enough.

Time after time, I saw how immigrant patients were the sickest of them all. How they would be discharged without even truly understanding the reason for admission in the first place, ignored when asked for an interpreter, or having their cultural requests taken seriously. As a Latina nurse, my name on that badge was like a signal to Spanish-speaking families that I was going to be truly there for them. When the pandemic in 2020 consumed us all, my community was suffering the most. I had no breaks after my shifts as I tried my best to pick up as many phone calls and answer a sea of text messages, such as, "I tested positive, should I sleep in my car? I don't want to get my Abuelita sick." "My dad is having trouble breathing, he's had a fever for days now, what should we do!?" "If I go to the hospital, do they have interpreters? I don't want to die alone." I was consumed by the questions and confusion from my community on how to survive this deadly virus. Many of my Latina nurse colleagues felt the world on their shoulders as well while trying to educate the community on a virus we had no idea how else it would impact us. We were exhausted at the end of our daily shifts, but we could not clock out from our duty as Latinas in healthcare. We owed it to our community. If not us, then who?

I knew we needed to do more for the Hispanic community, especially after seeing how COVID-19 had disproportionately affected our lives. I was sick and tired of seeing my community plead for help or regard for our cultural needs and experiences as Hispanic citizens. The years of advocating both inside and outside the clinical setting prepared me to establish the first Hispanic Nurse Association in Tennessee. In 2021, with support of friends and family, and so many Latina nurse leaders across the country, I founded The National Association of Hispanic Nurses–Tennessee

Chapter. Our mission as a chapter is to serve and advance the health of Hispanic communities and to lead, promote, and advocate the educational, professional, and leadership opportunity for Hispanic nurses.

FAVORITE NURSING MEMORY

My very last patient was a family friend. My dad had called me one early rainy morning asking if I could take them to their post-op appointment. I remember my dad saying, "Mija, no sabe de que es esta cita, puedes ir con el? I clearly remember being angry that this appointment would take up half of my day. I didn't want to spend another minute in a hospital setting, let alone on my day off, but I sighed and agreed. I picked up this family friend from his house, he slowly made his way down the flight of concrete steps outside the apartment building holding on to the rail so tightly as if his life depended on it and his other hand over his hip clearly in pain. When we arrived and I sat in the waiting room translating intake forms, I had a gut feeling that this was not just a simple post-op appointment. The forms and posters on the wall had the word "oncology" plastered everywhere. I finally asked: "Usted sabe por que estamos aqui?" He replied:" No, mija no se. Solo me dijieron que hoy tenia cita aqui."

Cancer. Stage 4. There's not much we can do, he doesn't have "papers." "Without health insurance, the best thing he can do is to go back to his home (country) and die." I felt my stomach drop. How can I translate this to a man who's been in the United States for the last three decades away from his family trying to provide the best for them and now this country is telling him to go *home* to die? This was his home. I couldn't look at him as I gave him the diagnosis. I could only see his head hung low and tears running down his face out of the corner of my eye. I knew that this system had failed him, we had failed him, we had lost another one of ours.

Becoming a nurse has been the best decision of my life. Although I am not clinically practicing as a registered nurse, this profession has opened many doors and opportunities for me to continue to fight and advocate for my community. The most valuable lesson I have learned as a nurse is never to be afraid to speak up and take up all the space needed to be heard. Our experience as Latinas is our superpower. We need more of us in nursing, in healthcare. The landscape is changing and our communities need to see themselves reflected in us. Although there will be times of discouragement, ground yourself in your why. Find mentors, seek other Latinas in healthcare and in science, technology, engineering, and math (STEM) fields, etc. Continue to build your community as you navigate this journey. There are so many people waiting to be cared for by you, continue to grow, and never let anyone discourage you from your reaching your dreams. As you navigate this journey of becoming a nurse, do not lose hope in yourself, be your biggest cheerleader. Nursing has never been a career for me, it's been so much more. It has been a calling.

BIOGRAPHY

Zacnité Vargas Avalos, BSN, RN is a passionate advocate for the immigrant community, a Registered Nurse, and President and Founder of the National Association of Hispanic Nurses–Tennessee Chapter. She has lived in Tennessee her entire life since immigrating from Mexico with her family over two decades ago. As a proud Latina, she recognizes the value and role her culture and ethnicity play in the medical field. As an undocumented immigrant, she has experienced barriers to equitable healthcare access and has made it her mission to provide culturally competent care and understanding wherever she goes. As a result, in 2021, she established the NAHN chapter in Tennessee. This chapter aims to build community among Hispanic nurses and address the health inequities Hispanic communities face today. The stories she has heard through community voices have inspired her to uplift lived experiences as a mechanism to challenge system processes to address health disparities in Tennessee.

Zacnité Vargas Avalos, BSN, RN

vargaszacnitetn@gmail.com

IG: @latinx_nurses or @nahn.tn

BECOMING THE CHANGE

MELISSA CORTEZ

"Remember, it only takes one idea executed at the right time in the correct way to change the world."

CURRENT POSITION

I am the Founder and CEO of Cortex Gold, Inc.

WHAT I LOVE ABOUT NURSING

I love the versatility of nursing. You can work in almost any setting, with any patient population or even on the administrative side and still feel like you are doing meaningful, purposeful work.

EMBRACING THE JOURNEY TO NURSING

I never wanted to be a nurse. Growing up when someone asked me what I wanted to do, I had one simple answer, "I want to change the world." I had no plan of how I was going to do that, I just knew it was what I was supposed to do. That quest began to become clearer one rainy fall day in my junior year of high school. My father, an accomplished business man and long-time practitioner of practicality, sat me down at our wooden kitchen table. He gently, but firmly slid a freshly printed Forbes magazine across the table where I read an article titled, "Top 10 Most In-Demand Careers." As I skimmed the list on the ear marked page, I knew what this conversation now meant. It meant that I had to give up my dream of being a marine biologist. I had spent hours imagining surfing the world, training dolphins, and saving sea turtles from trash. Now, I was hit with a wave of reality, I was going to pick a job on this list, especially if I wanted to cash in on my parents well-planned promise of no student loan debt. Unlike most of my colleagues, I never really had first-hand experience with healthcare. Other than a tonsillectomy at six years old, I never set foot in a hospital. But I knew my dad was right, so with a dorm room covered in surfing posters and Bob Marley T-shirts, I entered the pre-nursing track at Towson University in Baltimore, Maryland, in the fall of 2008. Little did I know, but this pivotal advice would point me in the direction of a tumultuous journey filled with not only job security, but immense joy and incredible grief. But more importantly, a chance to do just what I had wanted—change the world, one patient at a time.

Journeys always have been a part of my story. I was born in Colombia, in a time where millions of people were displaced due to a conflict fueled by a lucrative illegal drugs trade and greed. My young mother was unwed and forced to make a terrible decision to raise a child in a war-torn country or abandon me. She decided leaving me to the care of an orphanage in hopes that I would have a better life was the best course of action. Twenty-five years later, when I visited her and the home where I would have grown up, it became clear to me as I saw the immense poverty, lack of electricity, and running water that her decision was really the only loving option. Through adoption, my young birth mother's selfless choice blessed my American family with years of laughter, love, and for sure if you ask my parents, its fair share of challenges. I grew up in northern Maryland, a predominantly Caucasian area of the country. In fact, I faced a great deal of racism from kids that were just mimicking the uneducated views of their close-minded parents. My parents always made sure I knew that I was unique and loved. I learned that ignorance would never be challenged by anger, but through education and kindness.

College was my first chance to really embrace and understand my Latina roots. Through my membership in the Latin American Student Organization (LASO), I was able to learn about what it truly meant to be of Latin American descent. I heard the struggles that my fellow students faced growing up as migrants or as children of undocumented immigrants. I was able to blend the experiences I had growing up with what I learned about being Hispanic through my friends in college to create my own culture. Children who are adopted, especially to families of different ethnicities than their births, often form their own cultural identity. My biggest lesson was learning it's not what you look like or where you come from that determines your future. It's who you want to become and how hard you are willing to work to get there. College was more than a degree for me, it was where I was given the chance to form my own unique identity. I entered the nursing workforce knowing that I was born in hope, raised in love and that I had to live for the promise of the true American dream through the service of others.

Nursing has always been a selfless but rewarding way to serve others. For me, it was a balancing of karma, or maybe a way to deal with the guilt I often felt from being adopted. As my career in nursing progressed, I truly found joy in the art of being a critical care nurse. Early in my critical care career, I worked with one of the best pulmonology intensivists in the world. He was a challenging teacher, but an excellent physician. I attribute my success to his rigorous questioning and ceaseless thirst for knowledge. He taught me that there is always a reason why someone is getting sicker and a seasoned nurse's intuition will never fail you.

I was able to fuel my gypsy soul as a travel nurse. I got married and divorced, twice. Partially due to the demands that nursing placed on my personal life and caring for three young boys, but also because of the unhealed trauma and abandonment issues I unknowingly carried with me from my adoption. I was content with burying myself in nursing, caring for others, my boys, and looking for the next assignment. Then, COVID-19 hit.

I remember sitting on my couch playing blocks with my youngest son, who was just over a year, when the phone rang.

"Mel, it's MayLane. Are you watching the news? You won't believe what job is open. The rates are incredible." I put the TV on mute. It was my travel recruiter. I had been home working as a pro re nata (PRN) registered nurse while I navigated a divorce. Traveling was the furthest thought from my mind. "I would have to quarantine and leave the kids. I don't know, MayLane." I replied, stroking my son's soft curls.

"It's going to be bad, everywhere. Plus, it's only an eight weeker at 6 thousand dollars a week," she said, "You might as well go somewhere amazing that's on your bucket list and make a ton of money while you can."

As a military wife for twelve years, I had always been on the other side of duty's call. This time it was different. I hugged my small children goodbye and got on a very empty plane to Boston in March 2020. It was the hardest flight I have ever taken and one that changed my life forever.

PIVOTING FROM COVID-19 FEARS

The fluorescent lights in the intensive care unit (ICU) were starting to get to me as I stood at the head of the bed titrating the patient in room 3's pressors for what seemed like the hundredth time this shift. He was so unstable. It was like any slight adjustment, any slight repositioning of the pillow, or vent changes sent him into a hemodynamic spiral that was almost impossible to manage. It didn't help that we had run out of sedation that morning and the paralytics were still going. With sweat running into my eyes, I spoke to him softly. *"Come on Pierre. You have to make it through this. Don't you dare die on me today."* I had just held the tablet up for the last twenty minutes for his wife and kids to speak to him in French hoping that would help us both feel better. He was one of Haitian Creole patients I cared for in Boston, but most of the other patients were Hispanic.

At the height of the pandemic, we had 250 COVID-19 intubated patients in house. We would post their names on the doors and it ended up being nothing but a sea of Hispanic last names for twenty rooms in a row. It allowed us to grab supplies faster and for doctors to know who they were treating without entering the room. It wasn't a Health Insurance Portability and Accountability Act (HIPPA) violation since there were no visitors or vendors allowed inside. But that meant no translators either. I had learned a tremendous amount of Spanish in college and had traveled to Colombia a few times, so I translated a lot. My Spanish is far from perfect but the families were so appreciative and helped me as I struggled through my mask, tears, and word finding to do my best to bring them comfort by addressing them in their native language. I would ask them what music their loved one liked. I would play them bachata or corrido from my phone while I bathed them. I remember how my heart sank as I scrubbed their hands and could see their thick callouses from years of hard work fall off like winter snowflakes in my double gloved hands. That's what happens as your skin dies and you lie in a bed intubated for thirty-plus days.

After Boston, I continued to travel for the next two years in COVID-19 ICUs. I watched hundreds of people die. Some slowly, drowning to death on bipaps (a type of ventilator that helps with breathing), gasping for air, white knuckling the bedrails. Some bleeding from their endotracheal tube (placed between the vocal cords through the trachea to provide oxygen and inhaled gases to the lungs) as we coded them. I spent hours sweating in reused personal protective equipment (PPE). I saw the hopelessness and apathy on my colleagues faces as we coded patients, again, and again, and again. It seemed like no one lived. I am sure some did, but it never felt that way.

I don't exactly recall when the nightmares started. But I knew I needed help when I had a panic attack in my bathroom and I had to call my neighbor across the street to come get my kids. I didn't know at the time, but I was suffering from post-traumatic stress disorder (PTSD) and the tremendous amount of moral injury I had faced over the last few years. I sought help and realized that I couldn't be the only one. Turns out, I wasn't. I remember talking to my therapist who was treating hundreds of other nurses through a nonprofit that was started. I kept thinking that hospitals needed to take a bigger role in supporting our mental health so I started my first company, Cortex Energy Systems. I worked with experts to develop a neuroscience-based stress reduction program for hospitals to add to their learning module systems. But it was too late. Nurses were already leaving the bedside in droves and had almost zero interest in learning how to heal themselves. Hospitals certainly did not want to invest in "mindfulness" when their resources were struggling from the pandemic.

So, I did what any good entrepreneur does, I pivoted. I started researching the top reasons why my colleagues were leaving and most of them were large systems issues, like staffing and finances that I was never going to fix. But one issue, increased rates of violence seemed like something I might be able to do something about with the help of a community that I had come to love and respect, the United States Marine Corps.

Innovation in healthcare has always occurred at the bedside of our sailors, soldiers and marines. I knew that now, after fighting our own war that, these well-trained veterans would step up to help us, if I asked. And they did. With the help of a fellow Latino US Marine, I founded Cortex Gold, Inc., the first tactical healthcare company in the world. Our mission began with a way to create a standard for healthcare security. As we networked and grew, our mission became focused on not only helping to reduce workplace violence within healthcare but also school systems. Over 80 percent of the nursing workforce is female. There is a similar demographic with schools. We are both tasked with protecting a building full of vulnerable populations. We hope that our programs will be able to support both industries. I believe in the ability of veterans to not only teach us the skills needed to reduce violence at the bedside, but to use their training to help us protect our patients and their families from an increasingly violent world.

COVID-19 has changed our healthcare system forever. It has highlighted many of its issues, but it also has given nurses a voice and an opportunity to create meaningful change. If there's one thing that we as Latinas understand, it's that anything worth doing is going to be challenging. We are a community of women that care deeply for those we love, are passionate about the things we believe in, and are unstoppable as long as we have a goal. The key is to find that goal. For me, it's believing that I can help heal my profession through promoting a culture of safety. The infamous Florence Nightingale has a great saying that continues to bring me hope, "Nothing can be done in the spirit of fear." To me, she is saying don't let fear hold you back from continuing on your journey, even if you don't know exactly how to get there. Remember, it only takes one idea executed at the right time in the correct way to change the world.

FAVORITE NURSING MEMORY

Favorite nursing memory was saying goodbye to a young woman with Down syndrome that I cared for during the beginning of COVID-19. She was the only patient I had live on that unit in three months. She had been intubated for thirty-seven days; and when she was finally stable enough to go home, I remember there was not a dry eye in the unit. She was a symbol of hope for all of us. She was proof that despite it all—the death, the lack of PPE, the heartaches—it is all worth it for those we are able to heal.

BIOGRAPHY

Melissa Cortez, BSN, RN, graduated from Towson University in Towson, Maryland, with a Bachelor of Science in Nursing. As a critical care travel nurse for over ten years, she has been in many facilities across the country. After two pivotal years caring for patients in the COVID-19 pandemic, she then chose to leave critical care to launch Cortex Gold, Inc. and to create a solution for the rising violence at the bedside. She is a speaker, consultant, and founder of a Veterans Vocational Training Center, where she works to supply healthcare organizations with well-trained veteran resource officers. She lives in Austin, Texas, with her three boys, dogs and the love of her life.

Melissa Cortez, BSN, RN
melcortez@cortexgold.com
LinkedIn: Mel Cortez BSN, RN

NI DE AQUÍ, NI DE ALLÁ

KIM ANN KIM

"I have never had to face anything that could overwhelm the native optimism and stubborn perseverance I was blessed with."—Sonia Sotomayor

CURRENT POSITION

I am a diabetes nurse educator.

WHAT I LOVE ABOUT NURSING

I love that nursing science calls on all my senses to assess the person and environment and intuitively make adjustments to promote optimal healing. Sometimes, it is as simple as adjusting the lighting, fluffing a pillow, or placing my hand on theirs. My nursing practice is equal parts healing art and clinical science, and this is what makes us unique as nurses.

WHAT LIMITS US IS OUR DISBELIEF IN OUR ABILITIES

My earliest memories as a child were of my mother's hand reaching over the side of my crib to give me leche de chocolate in my Fred Flintstone bottle. I can still taste the plastic nipple that was rigid in the center from being cut open para que el cereal pueda pasar. In the background was a yellow night light that illuminated the gold-framed portrait of La Virgin de la Caridad del Cobre (the patron saint of Cuba).

I have many memories of plates of arroz con frijoles y picadillo, kisses on the cheeks when arriving or departing from friends and family, and late nights falling asleep on a row of chairs while the adults danced to salsa or slammed dominos down on the table at the Cuban Civic Center. We spent countless weekends there attending celebrations of baptisms, birthdays, quinceañeras, and weddings. The faces were every shade of black, brown, beige, and white and everyone spoke Spanish, lovingly greeted me with "Hola, mi vida" and knew exactly who I was, la hija chiquita de Chino y Jane.

Intermixed with those moments in time are memories of visits with my mom's family, white Americans who moved to Connecticut from Maine. My dad was never with us for those visits. Somehow my young brain knew that my Latinidad was checked at the door for me to pick up on the way out. English was spoken by everyone, and I felt at times I was on the edge looking in. Overhearing discussions about "those people" or my dad, I listened closer and would be told that they weren't talking about me, because I looked like them and not "those people." I recall sensing the tension and feeling conflicted about my identity in that space. I pondered how my maternal family felt about me, if I was an extension of my father and he was clearly not a fan favorite.

Those formational years often brought race, ethnicity, residential status, and othering into adult conversations around me, and my young mind looked left to view how society interacted with my white mother and then swung right to see how differently my brown dad was treated. I watched not only in the presence of family or friends but in stores and the drive-through at McDonald's. The way in which my dad was told to speak English, while he was speaking his best English, hurt me. I wondered why other people couldn't see him like I did or understand his English as I could.

I brought these two worlds that I existed in with me everywhere. In a way, I was two different versions of myself. *Ni de aquí, ni de allá.* My name itself would get me othered on a regular basis, but so would some recognition that I was not fully white from other whites, and not Latina enough from other Latinos. People would ask if I was a variety of ethnicities and then ask what I was. When I answered, I was invalidated and told I didn't look like who I was. It was not something my immediate family engaged in dialogue about, but my father instilled that I should be proud of my heritage, especially as a first-generation American from his side of the family. I was taught to regard my education as a privilege that others, like our family in Cuba, did not always have access to.

When I entered the nursing world, the dualism of my existence flew under the radar at first. As a young mother and a non-traditional-aged student, I felt again like I was on the periphery looking in. My professors were mostly white women, and it wasn't until a beautiful brown Latina professor walked into my clinical assessment lab (and rocked my world) that I noticed what I was missing. Representation. I recall looking at her name badge to confirm my assumption that she was Latina and my mind floated out of that lab up to the clouds where her face was beaming; and I realized—for the first time—that I could be successful in my nursing program and be like her, an educator.

I can say with confidence that my years in the undergraduate nursing program were the hardest of my life. Balancing studies with working to provide for my daughter was a challenge. I didn't have anyone to talk to about how hard it was or how my anxiety kept my stomach in knots. I was among the older students in the cohort and often felt that I did not belong. In my junior year, my mother transitioned, and I did not think I could continue. My grades slipped and I sought guidance from a faculty member. I was told I should consider dropping out. I was not offered support and was required to be back in class and at clinical within days of my mother's death. My clinical instructor that semester was the Latina professor (the only Latina faculty) and while she did not lower her expectations of me, she told me to fight through it because I could. And I did, in honor of my mom, Jane, and because I knew my daughter was watching.

I credit my angel, mom, and the grace of God for getting

me through the remainder of the program. I compartmentalized my grieving and was in disbelief that I completed the program. I studied hard for the National Council Licensure Examination (NCLEX-RN®) and was certain I would not pass. But I did. I was hired to start as a Registered Nurse on a medical floor and then I allowed myself to grieve the loss of my mother and spread her ashes in Maine as she wanted.

Among my new nursing colleagues, I again teetered under the radar and would quietly observe interactions, tones, and how Latino patients were treated. I didn't offer to explain my ethnicity but as time went on and I spoke Spanish with patients, my peers learned that I was, in fact, Latina. I wish I could say that stopped the hurtful comments about "those people," my people, or how they should speak English in this country, or go back to their own country if they didn't like how they were treated. It took a little time for me to find my voice. But once I did, I refused to tuck either half of me away. The poking from either side, pushing me back to the one-half that people thought I really belonged to grew old. Explaining my unique name became tiresome and I realized that although I was ni de aquí, ni de allá, I was both from here and there, and it was my superpower.

Although this form of liberation for my existence came in later years, I have found that it is the foundation of my nursing philosophy and emancipatory way of knowing (Chinn et al., 2022). I bring something special to nursing, knowing that to promote wellness, space is required for humans to be their authentic selves. This requires safety and a healthcare system that reflects the community.

Once I got my footing at the bedside and more comfortable advocating for patients I was privileged to care for, I looked for representation within the hospital. Again, most of the nursing staff within the hospital were white women, but the unit I was on was one of the most diverse. I was blessed to see nurses in different stages of their careers, some approaching retirement and having seen every new thing in nursing circle the block and come back as a new initiative. Others were pursuing advanced degrees in Masters of Nursing Education or Masters in Nurse Practitioner programs. Seeing colleagues balance work and graduate school encouraged me to consider my next academic steps.

I didn't know how to decide what those next steps would be for me. I knew I wanted to be around the table where decisions were being made, and I wanted to elevate the role of nurses at the bedside. I knew that we were the experts on the patients and their responses to medical treatment and nursing care. I knew that listening to patients and hearing their stories brought me joy. I felt so honored to be a part of their experience, whether they recovered from their illness or transitioned from their earthly experience. What would that translate to in a graduate degree?

After learning that a local university formed a partnership with my employer, I attended an information session and took another leap of faith. I applied for the Master of Science in Nursing (MSN) Program in the Clinical Nurse Leader track. Within a few months, I was enrolled and started classes in a hybrid model where classes were held at the hospital. My youngest child was nine months old and my oldest was starting high school. It was a fast two years, but I successfully completed the program and became the first person in my family, either side, to earn a graduate degree. I was the only Latina in my cohort.

With newfound confidence in my ability to achieve my dreams, I set my sights on a certification as a Diabetes Educator (now called Certified Diabetes Care and Education Specialist). I started networking with professionals who did the work I wanted to do and those who achieved the educational goals I had. I asked for guidance on how to be successful and sought out learning opportunities in leadership, diabetes management, and nursing education. I began to work part-time as a clinical instructor and found another version of joy in working with students. We learned together and we talked about all of nursing, the parts we struggled to reconcile, and the parts we wanted to improve.

In each of these settings, there was a lack of representation. In each setting, there was a lot of discussion around health disparities among Latinos and a lot of explaining poor outcomes as a choice my community made to surrender to poor health through unfortunate decisions and bad genetics. Again, this commentary was hurtful, and at no time did I see Latinos in leadership roles or making decisions about how to improve these disparities. The pain fueled me to keep speaking up and to build my toolbox so that I had what I needed to be heard and respected.

Where I am on a personal level today is very different from when I entered nursing. I am not the same Kim Ann Kim. I am not the same nurse. I found like-minded Latinos in nursing who felt like I felt and wanted to help our communities achieve health, gain respect, and be given the chance to share our gifts. I believe we have the tools, skills, and talent to turn disparities around and to elevate our voices as the largest growing population in the United States.

When I am asked what I wish my younger self knew, there are two words. You belong. The expressions of trust and comfort when I speak Spanish with patients and talk about their cultural foods and practices with love and affection, is worth more than gold. Helping others feel seen, something I desperately wanted for myself, is now something I do with great reverence. I tell every nursing student I meet that we need them, and I sincerely mean that. We need diversity in nursing. We need nurses like me who are *ni de aquí, ni de allá* so that others who live in duality, bilingualism, and bicultural spaces can exist freely, authentically, and fully.

In conclusion, I would like to remind people who, like me, come from complicated, perfectly imperfect humble beginnings that we are greater than our circumstances. The only thing that limits us is our own disbelief in our abilities. The narrative that we come from less than or worse than or are unworthy is the tale of the oppressors. Our poder will not be denied.

FAVORITE NURSING MEMORY

One of my favorite memories was volunteering at a vaccine clinic with my National Association of Hispanic Nurses (NAHN) Hartford Chapter colleagues. We worked with the local public health department to administer vaccines to residents of Hartford. We vaccinated hundreds of people that day, and what I remember is the sense of hope people felt. People were comforted that we were able to speak to them in Spanish and help to answer their questions. I walked away with a sore wrist and immense pride that we helped our community.

References

- Chinn, Peggy L., Maeona K. Kramer, and Kathleen Sitzman. *Knowledge development in nursing: Theory and process.* St. Louis, MO: Elsevier, 2022.

BIOGRAPHY

Kim Ann Kim, MSN, RN, CDCES, graduated from the University of Saint Joseph in 2009 and from Sacred Heart University in 2013. She is currently a Doctor of Nursing Practice and Psychiatric Mental Health Nurse Practitioner student at the University of Saint Joseph. Kim works clinically as a Certified Diabetes Care and Education Specialist at a federally qualified health center. She is a member of the National Association of Hispanic Nurses–Hartford Chapter. Kim was appointed to the Commission to Address Racism in Nursing for the 2023-2024 term. She participated in the Overdue Reckoning with Racism in Nursing project and was featured in the Caring Beyond the Grain documentary. She resides in Bloomfield, Connecticut, with her daughters Anissa and Jamilah, and fur babies, Zoey and Tommi.

Kim Ann Kim, MSN, RN, CDCES
Rnkimi@yahoo.com
LinkedIn: Kim Kim

Tina Loarte-Rodríguez, DNP, RN, CIC, CPPS, CPHRM

ABOUT THE AUTHOR

Tina Loarte-Rodríguez is dedicated to leaving the world a little better than she finds it. She is an eternal optimist who believes in the power of community, kindness, and growth.

Her professional experience includes teaching and over seventeen years of nursing in various healthcare settings and specialties. She is the Associate Director, Health Equity Measures at the YNHH / Yale Center for Outcomes Research and Evaluation (CORE). Tina works with talented clinical investigators, statisticians, analysts, computer scientists, economists, epidemiologists, management experts, and administrative staff, actively collaborating with national and international experts on health equity measures and outcomes research.

A first-generation college graduate, she is a graduate of Cornell University, University of Connecticut, and Quinnipiac University. A perpetual learner with a passion for innovation, health equity and advocacy, she is currently participating in the American Nurses Association's Innovation Accelerator Program and will be a fellow of the American Nurses Advocacy Institute in the fall.

Tina is a Hartford Business Journal Healthcare Hero Award and the Connecticut Nursing Association Excellence in Team Award winner. She is active with the National Association of Hispanic Nurses–Hartford Chapter; the Connecticut Nursing Association; and DNPs (Doctors of Nursing Practice) of Color. Tina has published several works and is a featured author in *Hispanic Stars Rising Vol. III.*

Tina works hard and she plays even harder. She loves dancing, traveling, and reading. An Afro-Latina Boricua, born and raised in the Bronx, New York, she now resides in Connecticut with her extremely supportive husband, their three phenomenal children, her father, and two rescue dogs.

Tina Loarte-Rodríguez, DNP, RN, CIC, CPPS, CPHRM
www.latinasinnursing.com
LinkedIn: Tina Loarte-Rodríguez
Instagram: latinasin_nursing

Made in United States
North Haven, CT
10 September 2023

41386465R00104